S320
Science: Level 3

The Open University

Infectious disease

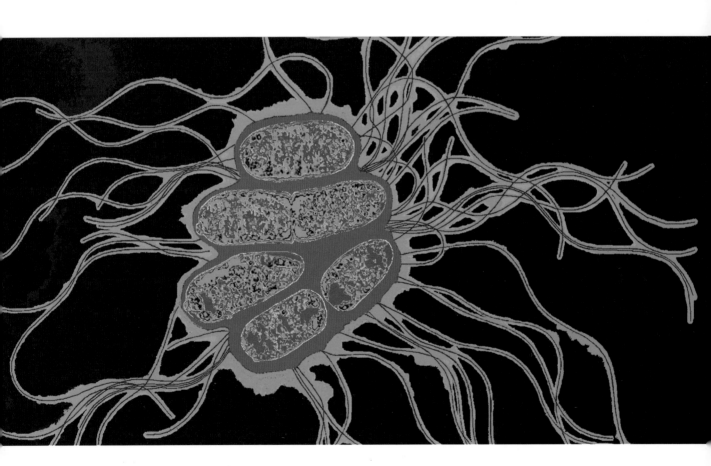

Book 7 Treatment and Control

Prepared for the Course Team by Basiro Davey, Bo Drasar,
Christine Heading, David Male and Ralph Muller

This publication forms part of an Open University course S320 *Infectious disease*. The complete list of texts which make up this course can be found at the back. Details of this and other Open University courses can be obtained from the Student Registration and Enquiry Service, The Open University, PO Box 197, Milton Keynes MK7 6BJ, United Kingdom: tel. +44 (0)845 300 60 90, email general-enquiries@open.ac.uk

Alternatively, you may visit the Open University website at http://www.open.ac.uk where you can learn more about the wide range of courses and packs offered at all levels by The Open University.

To purchase a selection of Open University course materials visit http://www.ouw.co.uk, or contact Open University Worldwide, Walton Hall, Milton Keynes MK7 6AA, United Kingdom for a brochure. tel. +44 (0)1908 858793; fax +44 (0)1908 858787; email ouw-customer-services@open.ac.uk

The Open University
Walton Hall, Milton Keynes
MK7 6AA

First published 2003. Reprinted 2008.

Edited and designed by The Open University.

Typeset by The Open University.

Printed and bound in the United Kingdom by The University Press, Cambridge.

ISBN 0 7492 5661 3

1.3

THE S320 COURSE TEAM

Course Team Chair

Michael Gillman

Course Manager

Viki Burnage

Course Team Assistant

Dawn Partner

Course Team Authors

Basiro Davey (Books 1 & 7)

Tim Halliday (Book 5)

Paddy Farrington (Book 6)

Michael Gillman (Books 1 & 5)

Hilary MacQueen (Books 2 & 4)

David Male (Books 1, 3 & 7)

Consultant Authors

Eric Bowers (Book 2)

Christine Heading (Book 7)

Laura Hibberts (Books 2 & 4)

Ralph Muller (Book 7)

Editors

Gerry Bearman

Pat Forster

Gilly Riley

Margaret Swithenby

Academic Reader

Mary Manley

External Course Assessor

Bo Drasar

OU Graphic Design

Roger Courthold

Sian Lewis

Video Editing

Wilf Eynon

Michael Francis

CD-ROM Production

Greg Black

Phil Butcher

BBC Production

Martin Kemp

Rights Executive

Christine Brady

Picture Research

Lydia Eaton

Indexer

Jean Macqueen

Course Websites

Patrina Law

Louise Olney

Sue Dugher

CONTENTS

1 CONTROLLING INFECTIOUS DISEASE

The first six books in the course and their disease case studies have presented a multidisciplinary account of our pathogens and parasites, their biology and their harmful effects on the human body, and our immune responses against them. You have learned about the impact of infection routes, virulence and other influences on the co-evolution of pathogens and host populations, each influencing the form and function of the other in an iterative process that continues endlessly from one generation to the next. We have described methods for the laboratory diagnosis of infectious disease and for modelling disease outbreaks in communities. This final book discusses the application of this knowledge to the huge task of combating infectious diseases and alleviating the suffering, disability and premature death they still inflict all over the world. Chapter 1 introduces the main themes and should take less than one hour to study.

1.1 The public health approach

In this book, we have chosen to discuss the treatment and control of infection in the context of measures aimed at improving the health of *populations*. Although we give many examples of medical interventions that treat or protect individuals, our approach is to focus on **public health**. This term encompasses the health of a population as a whole (or of a defined group within it, for example, all children under five years of age), and also the wide repertoire of strategies aimed at increasing a population's health.

○ Suggest some ways in which a population's health could be measured (think back to Book 1, Chapter 1).

● Some common indicators of population health are: life expectancy at birth, the infant mortality rate (deaths under 1 year per 1000 live births), the age-standardized mortality rate (all causes combined) per 100 000 population, and mortality and morbidity rates for specific diseases, disabilities or disorders.

○ Excluding the formal provision of health services, how can governments and local authorities directly intervene to control infectious disease in populations?

● Among the most important interventions are the provision of clean water to the whole population, the safe disposal of sewage and refuse, and measures to ensure the safety of food and other consumables sold to the public.

Less visible strategies that indirectly have a huge impact on population health are the provision of transport and other infrastructures to enable widespread access to health and social services, controls on the pollution of the environment by industrial processes, an education system that delivers a high rate of literacy in the population, an economic structure that supports an adequate income for all households, and a stable and equitable political system. At many points in this book we will refer to this wider public health agenda, while focusing most of our attention on strategies that directly control infectious diseases. As you will see, the professional discipline that also came to be known as 'public health' has always viewed the whole range of possible contributors to population health as its legitimate territory.

1.2 A brief history of public health

For most of history, human societies have had no means of preventing infection or curing infectious diseases. By the end of the eighteenth century, only two effective medical remedies were known: smallpox vaccination and the use of quinine as a preventive for malaria – though countless medicines were peddled or prescribed. As long as infection was seen as evidence of an imbalance in the patient's 'humours' or as due to the emanation of 'bad airs' (miasmas), no rational basis for treatment or control could be devised. Then a decisive development occurred in England in the 1820s. An inspirational group of philanthropists founded the *sanitary movement* or *sanitarianism*, with the aim of 'protecting the public health' from sickness, which they recognized arose primarily from the polluted urban environment of the period. The term 'public' encapsulates their focus on protecting the health of the population as a whole, rather than on treating or preventing disease in its individual members, and this emphasis remains central to public health strategies today.

England was the first country in the world to undergo industrialization in the nineteenth century, and a huge increase in mortality – much of it due to infectious disease – accompanied the rapid urbanization and unrestricted growth of 'slum' dwellings. The sanitarians were particularly concerned with the pollution of water sources and campaigned for local authorities to take responsibility for constructing sewers (Figure 1.1), disposing of refuse and providing clean drinking water to their populations. To support this aim, they collected systematic evidence of disease

FIGURE 1.1
This engraving from the *Illustrated London News* depicts the construction of London's main sewer; eighty miles of underground tunnels were built between 1858–65, discharging sewage from districts north and south of the Thames directly into the river.

outbreaks and associated factors such as overcrowding in houses, thereby establishing the discipline that subsequently became known as *epidemiology*. In the *Cholera* Case Study associated with Book 2, we highlighted the work of John Snow, who mapped cholera cases in a district of London in 1854 and traced the source to the Broad Street water pump. It was another three decades before Robert Koch isolated *Vibrio cholerae* and demonstrated the bacterial origins of the disease, but Snow's solution (removing the handle from the pump) brought the epidemic to a halt in a classic example of a public health intervention. As 'germ theory' became accepted from the 1890s onwards, it had a profound influence on sanitation policy in Western European countries and subsequently in North America and elsewhere.

Another major preoccupation of the sanitarian movement was the contamination of food sold to the public. The meteoric growth of the urban population led to a huge increase in demand for commercially traded food and a proliferation of shops, eating houses and street vendors, whose wares were often adulterated and filthy – as Tobias Smollet's description of milk sold in London at the end of the eighteenth century graphically illustrates.

> [the milk is] carried through the streets in open pails, exposed to foul rinsings discharged from doors and windows, spittle, snot and tobacco quids … the spewings of infants, who have slabbered in the tin-measure, which is thrown back in that condition among the milk, for the benefit of the next customer; and finally, the vermin that drops from the rags of the nasty drab that vends this precious mixture.
>
> (Quoted in Drummond and Wilbraham, 1939, p. 194)

Since the mid-nineteenth century, food-safety legislation and the system of inspection and enforcement initiated in the sanitarian period in the UK have proliferated, particularly in the advanced industrial economies, and have dramatically reduced the occurrence of food-borne infection. However, outbreaks of food poisoning remain a common occurrence even in countries with the most extensive public health regimes (as Chapter 4 will illustrate). Widespread improvements in the collection and disposal of refuse and sewage, and in the treatment and storage of water, have also delivered significant advances in public health in most parts of the world. As Book 1 described, these and other public health measures have reduced the global burden of infectious disease in every country to levels well below that experienced in Britain in the nineteenth century.

However, in the first half of the twentieth century, the accelerating pace of urban growth outstripped the capacity of poorer nations to provide clean water, sewage disposal and safe food for their populations, or to tackle other endemic sources of infection effectively. Concerns about the continuing burden of infectious disease in the aftermath of World War II led to the founding of the World Health Organisation (WHO) in 1946 to set a new and positive agenda for public health.

1.3 Public health strategies

A useful way of thinking about strategies to control infectious disease is to distinguish between four categories of intervention:

1   strategies that use chemicals to attack the pathogen;

2   strategies that promote resistance to infection in the host;

3   strategies that tackle an environmental source of infection;

4   strategies that isolate a source of infection to prevent it from being passed on.

▢   For each of the categories 1–4, suggest one example of an intervention to control a specific infectious disease.

▮   You may have chosen other examples, but here are some that you have already encountered earlier in the course:

1   Antibiotics and other antimicrobial drugs work by damaging the structure or altering the metabolism of their target pathogen; for example, penicillin interferes with the synthesis of the peptidoglycan layer on the surface of Gram-positive bacteria (see Book 2, Table 2.1).

2   Vaccination with an inactivated preparation of influenza virus increases resistance to subsequent flu virus infection, providing the infective strain is the same as (or closely related to) a component of the vaccine (see Book 1, Chapter 2).

3   The provision of bed-nets is a highly effective strategy for controlling the vectors of pathogens such as malarial parasites (Figure 1.2, and also see the *Malaria* CD-ROM associated with Book 1, Chapter 3).

4   Quarantine of infectious individuals has been practised for centuries, for example, in the isolation hospitals and TB sanitaria of the late nineteenth and early twentieth centuries (see the *Tuberculosis* Case Study, Section 1).

FIGURE 1.2
Insecticide-treated mosquito nets, particularly those that can be erected over outdoor sleeping mats as in this village in Ghana, offer effective protection from the mosquitoes that transmit malarial parasites (*Plasmodium* species).

Malaria was one of the infectious diseases at the top of the WHO's agenda from the outset. In 1955 an ambitious series of country-wide campaigns was launched to eradicate it by attacking its mosquito vectors with insecticides, principally DDT. However, the success achieved in parts of Europe and the Americas could not be sustained in Africa, Asia and countries of the Pacific rim. By the 1970s, lack of funding to drain mosquito breeding grounds, difficulties in organizing repeated spraying campaigns, concerns about the environmental effects of DDT, and the emergence of insecticide-resistant mosquitoes, forced the adoption of more modest goals to reduce the incidence of malaria. In Chapter 2 of this book, we refer to prophylactic drugs aimed at protecting individuals from malaria, as part of a wide-ranging discussion of chemical strategies for preventing and treating infectious diseases. The use of chemicals to treat contaminated drinking water or to disinfect food preparation areas makes an obvious contribution to public safety, but drug treatment of infected individuals also protects the public health.

◻ Can you explain how?

◼ Most (though not all) infectious diseases are communicable, so the medical treatment of individual patients reduces a source of infection which could spread to other susceptibles in the community. Thus, even the interventions we generally think of as 'medical' strategies aimed at curing individuals, are in a sense also public health measures.

Following the pioneering research of Louis Pasteur, who developed the first vaccine against rabies in 1885, steady progress was made in preparing vaccines against some other major diseases. Chapter 3 discusses issues of vaccine design, effectiveness and safety, and explains why some infectious diseases cannot yet be prevented by this method. By the 1950s, successful mass vaccination programmes were underway in parts of Western Europe (principally the UK and France) and in the USA, and from the 1970s onwards, the organisers of global public health initiatives against infectious diseases pinned their hopes on mass vaccination. The WHO's high profile campaign to eradicate smallpox achieved its goal in 1980 (the only disease to date which has been eradicated by vaccination), and targets were set to protect the world's children from the most common vaccine-preventable childhood diseases – initially measles, diphtheria, polio and whooping cough. The *Polio* Case Study provides further illustration of the issues discussed in Chapter 3, and traces the progress of the WHO campaign to eradicate polio globally by 2005.

Chapter 4 examines the breadth of the public health agenda in greater detail than we have attempted here in this opening discussion, and also illustrates the day-to-day work of public health provision by describing how a major outbreak of salmonella food poisoning was tackled in the UK. Since the 1990s, there has been renewed interest in low-cost public health initiatives involving community participation to tackle environmental sources of infection. In Chapter 5, we consider a highly successful campaign of this type to eradicate disease due to the guinea worm, *Dracunculus medinensis*. Throughout, we point to the willingness of the public health discipline to engage with socio-economic as well as environmental threats to health.

As you study the following chapters, note that the great diversity of infectious diseases and the varied life histories of pathogenic organisms means that effective interventions frequently require a combination of measures. Strategies that were once successful may be rendered useless by changes in the pathogen, the host or the environment. And there are clearly big differences in the cost implications of different strategies. For example, vaccination against tuberculosis is cheap by comparison with the provision of good housing and nutrition to a susceptible population. The social and health benefits of better housing and adequate nutrition extend far beyond the reduction of tuberculosis, but are out of reach of the majority of the world's population.

While there have been enormous strides in improving public health in all countries over the last century, there is still a huge gap between the health of the poorest (1.3 billion people with an income of less than US$1 per day live in absolute poverty) and the rest. Many developing countries now spend more on repaying international loans than on health and education combined, and in most the move to cities is advancing at a frightening pace, with all the threats to health that this entails. The WHO's *Global Water Supply and Sanitation Assessment: 2000 Report* (WHO, 2000) estimated that 1.1 billion people (one-sixth of the world's population) were without access to a safe supply of drinking water and 2.4 billion had no acceptable means of sanitation. We discuss the implications in Chapter 4.

However it is important to bear in mind from the outset that lack of funding – whether for improvement of social conditions, biological or pharmaceutical products, or to supply the essential infrastructure for delivering treatment and control programmes – is not the only barrier to protecting the public health. Pathogens can adapt very quickly under the selection pressure exerted by our attempts to control them. The geology and climate of a region may undermine efforts to provide clean water or dispose of sewage. Drought, floods, political conflict, warfare and terrorism displace communities into refugee camps where infection flourishes. There may be cultural objections to practices such as vaccination. Individuals and communities may be highly resistant to behavioural change.

In this final book, we describe a broad range of strategies for treating and controlling infection, but you should note that infectious disease is just one part of the public health agenda. The health effects of poor housing, industrial and agricultural pollution, food insecurity and malnutrition, tobacco, alcohol and illegal drugs, violence, accidents, sexual behaviour, impoverishment, unemployment and low pay, are all within the remit of public health.

Summary of Chapter 1

1   Public health strategies aim to prevent disease or reduce its impact by taking actions aimed at protecting or promoting the health of the population as a whole.

2   A systematic and evidence-based approach to addressing threats to public health, including water pollution, sewage disposal and food safety, began with the sanitarian movement in England in the 1820s, and accelerated once the 'germ theory' of infection was established in the 1890s.

3   Interventions against infectious diseases focus on one or a combination of four general strategies: chemical attacks on the biology of the pathogen, methods of promoting the resistance of the host to infection, tackling sources of infection in the environment, and isolation of infectious individuals.

4   The effectiveness of existing treatment and control strategies is frequently undermined by lack of funding for drugs, vaccines, environmental measures and the necessary public health infrastructure to deliver them. But impoverished social conditions, biological adaptation by pathogens, constraints imposed by geology and climate, and cultural and political factors, may all have adverse consequences for the control of infectious disease.

Learning outcomes for Chapter 1

When you have studied this chapter, you should be able to:

1.1   Define and use, or recognize definitions and applications of, each of the terms printed in **bold** in the text.

1.2   Select appropriate examples to illustrate public health strategies that (a) use chemicals to attack the pathogen; (b) promote resistance to infection in the host; (c) tackle environmental sources of infection, or (d) isolate infectious individuals. (*Question 1.1*)

1.3   Summarize the major constraints on delivering effective treatment and control strategies to protect the public health against infectious disease. (*Question 1.2*)

Questions for Chapter 1

Question 1.1

What public health strategies have reduced the *incidence* of TB to present-day levels, from its peak in Europe and North America in 1870–1880? (If you are unsure of the answer, refer to Figure 1.5 in Book 1, and revise Section 1 of the *TB Case Study* and the *Overview* screens of the associated CD-ROM, which you studied during Book 2. You will learn more about the treatment and control of TB when you complete additional work on the *TB Case Study* during Chapter 2 of this book.)

Question 1.2

What are the major constraints on delivering effective treatment and control of cholera in areas where it is still a major health problem? (If you are unsure of the answer, revise the *Cholera Case Study*, which you studied during Book 2.)

2 CHEMICAL STRATEGIES AGAINST INFECTION

This chapter builds on your understanding of the replication and life cycles of some key pathogens (and where relevant, their vectors), already discussed in Book 2 or in the case studies on malaria, tuberculosis, cholera and HIV. Here we review the diverse ways in which that knowledge has been applied in chemical strategies to treat infection inside the body or to control sources of infection in the external environment. Towards the end of this chapter, you will be referred out to the *Tuberculosis* Case Study where you will complete your study of TB by reading Section 6 and viewing part of the *Tuberculosis* CD-ROM.

DISCLAIMER: Information contained within this chapter does not imply a recommendation for the medical treatment of individuals.

2.1 Anti-infective chemicals

This chapter examines ways in which chemicals can be used to treat and control infectious diseases – building on strategies that have been going on for millennia. Abundant evidence from archaeological, anthropological and historical sources points to the extensive use by human cultures of **anti-infective chemicals** with actions against pathogens and parasites or alleviating their harmful effects on the body. Some have come from inorganic sources in the environment such as soils and minerals; others are plant-derived products. Examples that may go as far back as human history itself include the ingestion of clays to counteract the diarrhoea associated with food poisoning, the ingestion of plant-based medicines to kill gut parasites (see Box 2.1) or to combat fevers, and the use of aromatic plants to deter infection-carrying insects. For centuries food has been preserved in wines, spirits, salts or vinegar to prevent 'spoiling' by bacterial and fungal growths. Other examples that originate in the distant past include the addition of common salt by priests to consecrated water to keep it 'usable' for months, and the inclusion of hop extracts in beer to prevent the growth of unwanted organisms during the brewing process.

| BOX 2.1 | Pulvis catharticus pro Pueris, *A purging Powder for Children* |

Take Rhubarb, Rosin of Jalap, and Calomel, of each equal parts; Loaf Sugar the Weight of the whole. These ought all to be powder'd separately and very fine. The Sugar is a sufficient Corrector, and the whole makes not only a pleasant, but an efficacious and safe Purge for all Children; for they are always more or less subject to slimy Humours, and from thence proceed Worms in the Belly, which this wonderfully cleanses away and destroys. It may be given from 10 grains to a scruple. To grown Persons likewise in many Cases it is a good Cathartic, and may be increased from 1 to 2 scruples in a Bole, or mix'd in a thin Syrup, otherwise the Calomel will endanger being lost, by falling to the bottom.

From: *Pharmacopoeia Officinalis et Extemporanea* or *A Complete English Dispensatory*, 9th edition, published in London, 1733.

Prior to 1800, the use of chemicals to treat or control human disease was empirically based (i.e. based on observation or experiment), but the only truly effective chemical remedy against an infectious agent was the ingestion of cinchona tree bark extract (which contains quinine) as a preventive against malaria. From the nineteenth century onwards, chemical intervention was increasingly based on theoretical knowledge of chemical reactions, the human body and the 'germ theory' of infectious disease, supported by experimental and clinical observations. The timeline featured in Box 2.2 indicates some of the landmark events in the history of the use of chemicals for anti-infective purposes.

BOX 2.2	Some landmark events from the history of anti-infective chemicals in Western cultures

Empirical use of anti-infectives	pre-history to 1800, beneficial use of substances, including:	salt, alcohol, vinegar, clays, mercurial salts and plant-based products (including cinchona for malaria and other fevers, ipecacuanha for amoebic dysentery, aspidium for tape worms)
Theory-based use of anti-infectives	1820	isolation of quinine from cinchona bark as an antimalarial remedy
	mid-1800s	use of chlorinated lime for handwashing in maternity wards
	1860	use of carbolic acid sprays and solutions during surgery
	1877	demonstration that some microbes antagonize growth of *Bacillus anthracis*
	1904	trypan red was found to reduce reproduction of *Trypanosoma equipodium*; use of the arsenic product atoxyl for skin infections
	1910	efficacy reported of arsphenamine (Salvarsan) against syphilis spirochaetes
	1929	antimicrobial actions of *Penicillium* genus moulds reported
	mid-1930s	Prontosil and sulfanilamide used as antibacterial agents
	1940	extraction and clinical use of penicillin
	1944	DDT patented in USA as an insecticide
	1944–53	streptomycin, neomycin, chloramphenicol and tetracyclines discovered and developed as antibacterials
	1952	isoniazid developed for TB treatment
	1970	rifampicin developed for TB treatment
	1986	zidovudine (first nucleoside analogue reverse transcriptase inhibitor) used against HIV
	1987	ivermectin (first oral drug to treat 'river blindness')
	1989	mefloquine used as an antimalarial
	mid-1990s	aciclovir used against herpes viruses; nevirapine (non-nucleoside reverse transcriptase inhibitor) and ritonavir (protease inhibitor) used against HIV
	2000	streptogramins developed for use against multi-drug resistant bacteria
	2003	miltefosine distributed in India to treat visceral leishmaniasis

A striking feature of Box 2.2 is the scale of the advance in chemical treatments since the discovery of penicillin in the 1930s. By 2002, the total number of manufactured pharmaceutical products licensed for human prescription in the USA had exceeded 3400 (United States Pharmacopeia-National Formulary). In this chapter, we are concerned only with chemicals that have some impact on infectious disease, but before we focus on the consequences of their success it is worth noting the gaps in the chemical arsenal.

Most of the chemical agents used in medical treatment act either against bacteria or against parasites. By comparison, there are relatively few antiviral drugs available, and (at the time of writing in 2003) *none* of them can eliminate viruses from the body, so there are no 'curative' chemical treatments for *any* viral disease. Moreover, even where anti-infective drugs exist, there may be significant problems with efficacy, toxicity and access. For example, some of the most damaging parasites affecting humans (including those causing malaria, sleeping sickness, Chagas' disease and leishmaniasis) are difficult to treat chemically; in some cases, the efficacy of available drugs is inadequate, particularly where resistant strains have evolved, or the toxicity of a drug in humans is the problem, or the drugs may be too expensive or in short supply for those who need them most. And, as discussed in several earlier parts of this course, bacterial drug-resistance poses new threats to health from pathogens that were formerly readily treatable by antibiotics.

However, problems of toxicity and drug-resistance are less important on the world scale than lack of access to chemical treatments that are widely available only in the richer countries.

2.1.1 Defining chemical actions against infection

In countries like the UK, a large number of chemicals are purchased for use in domestic situations with the aim of reducing the risk of infection.

- ☐ What chemicals do you use routinely in your home, which are advertised as acting against potentially harmful organisms in the domestic environment?

- ■ You probably use some of the following: bleach poured down sinks and toilets, bathroom cleansers incorporating disinfectants, antibacterial washing-up liquids and aerosol sprays to clean refrigerators and kitchen worktops. If you have a baby in the house, you may have used 'sterilizing' tablets or fluids to clean feeding bottles. Perhaps you have purchased dustbin liners and kitchen utensils made from plastics that have been impregnated with antibacterial chemicals. If you make pickles and jams at home, then you are using vinegar and sugar to preserve stored foods from microbial contamination.

- ☐ What types of product can be bought 'over the counter' for application directly to the skin, which claim to reduce the risk of infection?

- ■ A large range of products are available including: antiseptic solutions or creams to put on minor cuts and burns, 'germicidal' plasters to cover small wounds, chemically impregnated wipes for use during nappy-changing, antibacterial hand-washing liquids and facial cleansing lotions, antifungal powder to treat 'athlete's foot', 'medicated' shampoos, and many more.

Several of the terms used above – for example, *disinfectant, antiseptic, antibacterial* – occur in everyday language and in advertising widely available products, and also belong to an extensive professional vocabulary describing the ways in which chemicals can be used beneficially in infection control and treatment. These terms are commonly used with varying degrees of accuracy in the public and professional literature, so we begin by clarifying their meaning. But you should note that some definitions are not as clear-cut as you might suppose and there may be no 'right' or 'wrong' definition. Like language in general, the chemical vocabulary has changed over the years and terminology can be used differently in different situations and professional disciplines and in different countries.

To avoid misunderstandings, professional bodies publish guidelines on the usage of medicinal and chemical terminology. Sometimes they have to construct their own definitions for certain terms and keep redefining them as the need arises. In the USA, for example, the Food and Drug Administration (the FDA, the body with responsibility for food and medicinal legislation) issues its own definitions of terms such as *disinfectant* and *antiseptic*, which might have been thought to be universally understood. The approach in this chapter will be to use consensus definitions recognized in the UK by health care and related workers. If you encounter the terms being used differently elsewhere, it is best to focus on the point that the originator is trying to make, rather than waste effort on challenging the validity of a turn of phrase. A handful of terms that are particularly prone to conflicting definitions are described in the rest of this section, but others that might not be familiar will be defined later as the need arises.

First, consider the meaning of **therapy**. Used without any qualification, therapy covers any treatment for a medical condition that has already developed, regardless of the treatment modality – for example, surgery, drug treatment, counselling and rehabilitation exercises are all therapies. In the context of this chapter, we are concerned with **chemotherapy**.

○ What do you understand by chemotherapy?

● This general term has become associated in everyday usage with aggressive use of chemicals in cancer treatment. Literally 'chemotherapy' could apply to all drug-based therapy, but it is conventionally applied to the use of chemicals to kill or damage cells *within* a host that are regarded clinically as 'alien'. The targets for chemotherapeutic agents thus include cancer cells, parasites, viruses, bacteria, fungi and prions (though there are no agents currently available to combat the latter).

A **medicine** is a product formulated to deliver a chosen dose of active ingredient into the body by a chosen route, for example, it might be a solution for injection, a solid dosing form such as a tablet or capsule, or a liquid suspension for swallowing. Medicines have been prepared in palatable formulations since ancient times (Box 2.1 earlier, and Figure 2.1). The distinction is usefully made between medicines acting *inside* the body, and the therapeutic use of chemicals that act *outside* it (the subject of Section 2.1.3).

Another term we need to establish from the outset is **prophylaxis** – the preventive use of medicinal products or procedures to reduce the risk of developing a disease or disorder, or to reduce the risk of adverse events if it does develop. Thus, vaccination programmes to prevent infectious disease (the subject of Chapter 3) are a form of prophylaxis, which not only protects individuals but also contributes to

FIGURE 2.1
In this fifteenth century woodcut, an apothecary uses a pestle and mortar to grind feathers and other medicinal ingredients brought to him by the snakes that came to symbolize his profession. Illustration from *Ortus Sanitatis* published in Mainz in 1491.

public health. So, too, is the administration of drugs to people who are well, but at high risk of developing an illness; such chemical treatments are sometimes referred to as *prophylactic chemotherapy* or *chemoprophylaxis.*

☐ Suggest examples of chemoprophylaxis against an infectious disease.

■ You may have thought of the administration of antibiotics to people who are about to undergo major surgery to reduce the risk of post-operative bacterial infection. Anti-malarial drugs are taken for at least a week before travellers depart for a region where there is a risk of being bitten by mosquitoes carrying the malarial parasite. (We discuss prophylactic chemotherapy in more detail in Section 2.8.)

There are many ways in which the chemicals used to treat or prevent infection are categorized, and the same substance can be described by several different terms that focus on (for example) its chemical structure, its origin, the target organisms that it acts against, and so on. Box 2.3 sets out a taxonomy of different ways in which anti-infective chemicals can be described.

BOX 2.3	A taxonomy of descriptive terms for anti-infective chemicals
A chemical can be categorized by:	
the type of target organism it affects	generically: e.g. antibacterial, antiviral, antifungal, antiparasitic; or specifically: e.g. antitubercular, antimalarial, etc.
its spectrum of activity against a range of organisms	broad spectrum or narrow spectrum
its mode of action against the target organism	e.g. antimetabolite, surfactant, reverse transcriptase inhibitor, interferon, etc.
the origin of the drug	e.g. antibiotic (used strictly, means derived from biological sources, originally these were moulds); biological (a product derived from culture of genetically manipulated cells)
the chemical structure of the drug	e.g. a sulfonamide, an alcohol, a nucleoside analogue, etc.
the clinical purpose of the drug	e.g. anti-infective, anti-inflammatory, immunostimulant, prophylactic, chemotherapeutic, etc.
the side effects of the drug in patients	e.g. psychotoxic (some antimalarials can be mood-altering); ototoxic (some antibacterials may cause damage to hearing and/or balance)

Notice that in Box 2.3 there are no consistent rules about whether terms such as 'antibacterial' or 'antiparasitic' are hyphenated; we have chosen *not* to insert hyphens unless it is the most common practice to do so. Note also that many of the terms that are (strictly speaking) descriptive adjectives, such as 'antiviral' or 'anti-inflammatory', are frequently used as nouns in pharmaceutical and medical parlance – so, drugs that act against viruses are commonly referred to as 'antivirals', a doctor may prescribe 'an anti-inflammatory' for a patient, and so on. The most familiar example is 'antibiotic', but this term has many problems, as we now briefly describe.

2.1.2 Antibiotics and antibacterials

Everyone has at some time taken a drug described as an **antibiotic**, but the meaning of the term has become blurred over time. It originally signified the *biological origin* of the active chemical (e.g. penicillin is derived from a mould), not the fact that its targets are biological entities. Because the early antibiotics offered such a dramatic advance over therapy with synthetic anti-infective drugs, the term 'antibiotic' implied a therapeutic as well as a chemical difference. However, in the present day these associations no longer apply. Firstly, bacteria can become resistant to antibiotics, so the term no longer implies a therapeutic advantage over other drugs. Secondly, genetic engineering and advances in chemistry have led to the development of derivatives of natural antibiotics, so a clear distinction between a 'natural' and a 'synthetic' origin cannot be made.

Furthermore, we noted (in Book 2, Section 2.2.1) that 'antibiotic' is often used more loosely today to include all medicines that attack bacteria inside the body, and (though purists object) it has sometimes been extended to medicines with activity against other microbes. To avoid misunderstanding, national publications such as the *British National Formulary* (see Box 2.4) have abandoned the term antibiotic in favour of **antibacterial**. This target-based term applies to any chemical that can kill or suppress the growth of bacteria, regardless of whether it acts against bacteria in the environment or as a medicine within the body.

BOX 2.4   The British National Formulary (BNF)

The BNF is prepared by a committee of experts and published jointly by the British Medical Association and the Royal Pharmaceutical Society of Great Britain. It provides comprehensive advice on a wide range of chemical preparations in therapeutic use, their limitations and relative merits. It is under continuous revision and a new edition is produced in March and September each year for distribution primarily to doctors and pharmacists working for the NHS. Other countries produce their own formularies, e.g. the United States Pharmacopeia-National Formulary, mentioned earlier. A link to the BNF website appears under *Course Resources* on the S320 website.

2.1.3 Biocides

Biocides are anti-infective chemicals that act *outside* the body, either on the skin or other externally accessible surfaces (e.g. the eyeball, nasal cavity, mouth, vagina, rectum), or on inanimate surfaces in the environment (e.g. instruments, table tops, floors, etc.). These chemicals are never ingested or injected. Biocides act by *killing* potentially harmful microbes (the suffixes *–cide* or *–cidal* denote killing, e.g. a biocide that kills bacteria is described as **bactericidal**). At sub-lethal concentrations, bactericides generally also have some **bacteriostatic** activity in that they may prevent surviving organisms from replicating, thereby suppressing microbial growth (the suffixes *–stat* or *–static* denote the cessation of growth or motion, e.g. a *sporistat* is a biocide that prevents microbial spores from developing into replicating cells).

○ Earlier in the chapter, we asked about chemical solutions in common use in domestic situations to reduce the risk of infection. Which of them could be described as biocides?

■ Disinfectants, antiseptics and sterilizing fluids are biocidal against at least some pathogens. The term also includes preservatives added to products to prevent microbial growth.

We will briefly review the actions of biocides in each of these four categories, but note that some chemicals belong to more than one category and can be used in different ways for different purposes. All of them are defined by the circumstances in which they are *used* rather than by the chemicals involved.

Disinfectants

Chemicals that reduce the microbial contamination of an *inanimate* object or surface are described as **disinfectants**. Household bleach and similar chemicals are powerful disinfectants, and although they are not marketed with this label, they have advertising slogans such as 'kills all known germs'. The assumption is that disinfectants act rapidly and efficiently, but a particular agent may not adequately damage all the target organisms in all circumstances (bacterial or fungal spores, for example, are often unaffected). Chemical disinfectants tend to have a wide spectrum of activity against living cells, so they are unsuitable for application to the body. Disinfection can also be achieved by physical means such as exposure to X-rays or ultraviolet light.

Antiseptics

Antiseptic chemicals also reduce microbial contamination, but they are formulated for use on the externally accessible surfaces of the body. They are commonly included in mouth washes, face washes, soaps and throat lozenges, as well as being available in solution (e.g. Dettol) for domestic application. Alcohols (such as the ethanol in 'alcoholic' drinks) have antiseptic properties and are the principal ingredients in the preparations currently recommended for hand washing in hospitals to reduce the risk of cross-infection. (In Section 2.3.2, we look at the chemical structure of alcohols and relate this to their antiseptic action.) The term 'antiseptic' originated in the eighteenth century, but its meaning has changed over time. It derives from the Greek 'against putrefaction' and originally referred to agents that prevented spoilage of foods. It acquired its present meaning during the late nineteenth and early twentieth centuries, when the pioneers of 'aseptic' surgery employed chemicals such as carbolic sprays to reduce post-operative infection. (Book 2, Chapter 1 defined aseptic as free of harmful organisms.)

Before moving on, a word of caution is needed to alert you to a relatively recent development in the terminology. **Microbicide** has come to mean an antiseptic applied intra-vaginally or intra-rectally (e.g. in a biocidal gel or foam) to kill sexually transmitted pathogens such as *Chlamydia trachomatis*, *Neisseria gonorrhoeae* or HIV. Condoms may incorporate microbicides, and because many of these chemicals are designed to kill sperm as well as pathogens, the combination of antiseptic and contraceptive action in microbicides is likely to become implicit in the term.

Sterilizing fluids

Sterilization refers to the eradication of all forms of life from an inanimate object, but the term especially applies to microbes, as reflected in the definition used by the American Food and Drug Administration (FDA): 'a process intended to remove or destroy all viable forms of microbial life, including bacterial spores, to achieve an acceptable sterility assurance level'. The acceptable *sterility assurance level* or SAL is in turn based on a definition of *sterility* as a probability of less than one in a million that an organism could survive the sterilization process. An acceptable SAL may be set at a lower probability than one in a million, depending on the pathogen and the intended use of the sterilized object. Immersion in chemical sterilizing fluids is one method of decontaminating some types of medical equipment, but strong solutions must be used for long periods to achieve an acceptable SAL. For equipment that can withstand it, sterilization is more reliably achieved by exposing the object to very high temperatures (e.g. autoclaves sterilize their contents in super-heated steam).

Preservatives

A **preservative** is an agent that inhibits the growth of microbes capable of causing biological deterioration of a substance or material. Chemicals such as alcohol, sugar, vinegar and common salt have been used in human societies for centuries to prevent deterioration of foodstuffs during storage. Many synthetic preservatives have been developed for addition to foods, and others are ingredients of medicinal preparations such as creams, ointments and lotions applied to the skin or other body surfaces. For preparations such as eye drops, where the presence of harmful microbes could be especially serious, contamination of the initially-sterile drops during the usage period (a few days) is prevented by the inclusion of preservatives.

Summary of Section 2.1

1   Human cultures have a long history of using biocidal chemicals outside the body to combat infection, including alcohol, vinegar and salt employed as disinfectants, antiseptics or preservatives. From the 1800s onwards, the formulation of biocides and of chemotherapeutic or prophylactic medicines has increasingly been based on theoretical as well as empirical knowledge of chemistry and the biology of hosts and their pathogens.

2   The terminology used to describe the actions of anti-infective chemicals can vary between disciplines, regulatory authorities and countries, and may focus on the identity of the target organism, the origin or chemical structure of the agent, its spectrum and mode of action, its clinical purpose or its side effects.

2.2 Selectivity

Implicit in the discussion above has been the understanding that anti-infective chemicals will not damage all living cells equally. The **selectivity** of chemical agents is fundamental to the success of interventions as diverse as chemotherapy for a bacterial chest infection, the disinfection of contact lenses, and the use of insecticides to control the spread of malaria by its mosquito vectors. The selectivity of an anti-infective chemical has two components:

- The *spectrum of activity* of the chemical against a range of pathogens and its *efficacy* against susceptible organisms;

- The *selective toxicity* of the chemical, i.e. its ability to damage the target pathogens without causing collateral damage to host cells, commensal organisms in the host, or harmless organisms in the environment. (Selective toxicity was introduced in Book 2, Section 2.2.1.)

We will look at each of these aspects in turn.

2.2.1 Spectrum of activity and efficacy

It is customary to indicate how many different types of organism are damaged by a chemical agent by referring to its **spectrum of activity**. Put simply, a chemical that kills a wide range of organisms under normal usage conditions is said to have a *broad spectrum*, and one that kills only one or a few types has a *narrow spectrum*.

Chemical agents also vary in their **efficacy**, i.e. their ability to kill or prevent the replication of the organisms within their spectrum. There is no absolute measure of efficacy; different indicators are used in different situations, depending on the aim of the chemical intervention. Invariably, measurements of efficacy take account of the concentration and dose of the chemical, the length of exposure to it, and the outcome. Outcomes can be framed in terms of directly measurable effects on the target microbes (e.g. a commonly-used index of efficacy is the time taken to kill all the target organisms, or achieve complete stasis in their growth), or in terms of resolution of symptoms in treated patients, or (at its most extreme) the saving of human life.

As a generalization, it can be said that the spectrum of activity of a chemical and its efficacy determines its pattern of use.

Broad spectrum agents provide versatility: for example, some disinfectants (like phenol) are highly effective against viruses as well as prokaryotic and eukaryotic pathogens in the environment; antibacterial drugs such as amoxicillin are used to treat a wide range of bacterial infections in the community. However, you should note that even the broad spectrum agents (particularly those used *inside* the body) exhibit some selectivity for the pathogens they attack – amoxicillin is a broad spectrum antibacterial, but it has no effect against fungi, prokaryotic parasites or viruses; antiviral drugs are usually only effective against viral infections, antifungals only damage yeasts and moulds, etc. Although some broad spectrum chemicals are highly effective across their target range (for example, the antifungal drug, amphotericin B), many are not equally effective against all the pathogens within their spectrum. Thus, the efficacy of an antibacterial agent may vary across the spectrum of its target bacteria – some species are highly susceptible to it, others may be less so.

By contrast, **narrow spectrum agents** are effective against a few specific targets, which are either highly resistant to, or are not sufficiently controlled by, the broad range drugs. For example, the antiviral medicine aciclovir is highly selective for herpes simplex and varicella zoster, and its efficacy against these targets is better than any broad spectrum antiviral currently available (at the time of writing in 2003). However, it would be a mistake to assume that 'narrow range' always means greater efficacy: some narrow spectrum agents have relatively low efficacy against their targets (for example, the antiretroviral agents used to treat HIV infection do not eliminate the virus), but they are prescribed because they are the best currently available treatment.

○ Would you expect broad spectrum or narrow spectrum anti-infectives to have a larger share of the pharmaceutical market, and why?

● More research effort goes into developing broad spectrum agents, simply because they can be used to treat a wider range of infections, so they are often more useful to clinicians (particularly in general practice, the advantages of a small range of broad-spectrum agents compared with a large range of narrow-spectrum agents is obvious), as well as more profitable to the pharmaceutical industry. Relatively little effort is made to develop narrow spectrum drugs, unless the existing broad spectrum agents have proved to be ineffective and there is a large potential market for a chemical intervention.

Contact-lens disinfection

The importance of investigating the spectrum of activity of a therapeutic chemical can be illustrated by two studies of contact-lens disinfection, which took contrasting approaches. Inadequate disinfection of contact lenses enables a wide range of organisms to contaminate the lens (Figure 2.2) and cause microbial **keratitis** (inflammation of the cornea), which – if left untreated – can cause severe damage to the eye, even blindness. Rosenthal *et al.* (2000) reported a laboratory study assessing the efficacy of a new disinfecting solution for contact lenses, against common organisms known to be associated with keratitis. The antimicrobial efficacy was determined against 51 organisms, including several Gram-positive and Gram-negative bacteria, yeasts, moulds and *Acanthamoeba* (these protoctists were described in Book 2, Section 5.4.2). The study concluded that the new solution showed adequate destructive activity against the required broad spectrum of organisms.

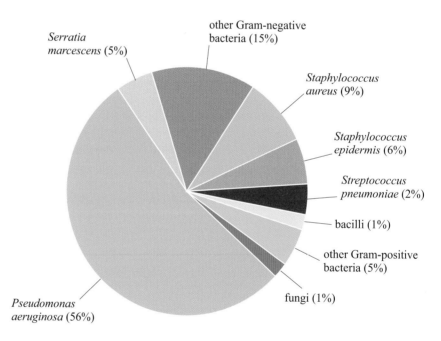

FIGURE 2.2
Survey of microbes associated with microbial keratitis in contact-lens wearers.

In the second study, Radford *et al.* (2002) approached the issue of selectivity from a different angle. They used an epidemiological approach to see whether the spectrum of activity of various contact-lens disinfection systems was sufficient to include efficacy against *Acanthamoeba*. Keratitis caused by this organism is a relatively rare condition (about 1.2 cases per million population in the UK), and the study tried to establish how and why users of re-usable contact lenses suffered from acanthamoebal keratitis. Amongst other findings, these authors reported that use of some disinfectant treatments (one-step hydrogen peroxide and chlorine-release soft-contact-lens disinfection systems) seemed to correlate with high prevalence of infection, whilst use of other regimens did not. It was already known that chlorine-based disinfection is effective against many relevant organisms, but not against *Acanthamoeba*. In contrast, hydrogen peroxide can be shown to be highly effective against *Acanthamoeba* in laboratory tests. The authors concluded, however, that the one-step hydrogen peroxide disinfection systems, under conditions of everyday use, were failing to kill *Acanthamoeba*.

☐ Suggest an explanation for the contradictory results obtained by Radford *et al.* on the efficacy of hydrogen peroxide against *Acanthamoeba*. Does your explanation have any implications for the results obtained by Rosenthal *et al.*?

■ Radford's results suggest that a disinfection system that is effective against a particular organism under laboratory conditions can be ineffective in conditions of everyday use. Unless new products are laboratory tested in conditions that simulate careless or hurried 'real life' use, then conclusions such as Rosenthal's about the efficacy of a new disinfection solution against a broad range of targets may not be borne out in practice.

Publication of findings from studies such as those highlighted above usually result in a review of efficacy and usage guidelines by the manufacturers of chemical products and by national medicines' regulators. If the available evidence is sufficiently strong, then it may result in the withdrawal of some products and/or the revision of usage-guidelines.

2.2.2 Selective toxicity

Protecting the host

It is obvious that anti-infective chemicals must not cause significant harm to the people who ingest them, or use them as biocides. It is worth remembering that the potential for damage is not only due to any directly toxic effects of the chemical on human tissues and body fluids, but may also arise as a result of allergic reactions. Although not always easy to achieve, the importance of **selective toxicity** – avoiding damage to the host (and other non-target organisms), while eliminating the pathogen – is emphasized in the opening sentence of the paper by Rosenthal *et al.* considered above:

> There has been increasing awareness of the need for more powerful contact lens disinfectants, ideally having low toxicity and allergenicity to ocular tissue.

(Abstract, Rosenthal *et al.*, 2000)

This statement is a contemporary example of the selective toxicity principal pursued by Paul Ehrlich (1854–1915) and others, a hundred years earlier. Ehrlich is often regarded as the founder of modern chemotherapy, and his aim was to find and characterize dyes that would damage invading organisms, but leave human tissues and functions undamaged. His goal of identifying chemicals that performed like a 'magic bullet' aimed at infecting organisms has underpinned the search for chemotherapeutic agents ever since. Ehrlich attempted to quantify selective toxicity by devising a 'chemotherapeutic index', which he designated as the ratio of:

$$\frac{\text{minimal curative dose}}{\text{maximum tolerated dose}}$$

Erlich considered a ratio of 1:5 as an acceptable threshold for selective toxicity in patients, but although the concept of the index was a major step forward at that time, it is now seen as too simplistic. (Question 2.2 at the end of this chapter asks you to explain why – you should be able to give a complete answer by that stage.)

The first drug widely regarded as claiming the 'magic bullet' accolade was Salvarsan 606 (the brand name under which the chemical arsphenamine was marketed; see Box 2.5). Salvarsan 606 was an arsenic-based drug effective against *Treponema pallidum*, the spirochaete bacterium that causes syphilis. Ehrlich tested and retested more than 600 arsenic compounds, until an appropriate dose of the 606th chemical was shown to kill syphilis spirochaetes without causing significant harm to infected patients.

BOX 2.5   Brand names and generic drug names

In scientific and medical literature it is normally preferable to use the chemical name for the active principle in a medicine or other therapeutic product – often referred to as the **generic drug** name (e.g. arsphenamine). This avoids the confusion that can arise if the **brand name** (e.g. Salvarsan 606) is used instead, because similar medicines can be marketed under different brand names by different pharmaceutical companies, and (to make matters worse) different medicines can be marketed under the *same* brand name by one company in different countries! If it is particularly important to state the brand name, then the generic drug name should also be included.

Protecting commensal microbes

The importance of avoiding damage to non-target organisms as a side-effect of chemical treatments and control strategies has become increasingly recognized. Standards of selective toxicity aim to minimize harm to commensal organisms within the human body.

○ What adverse consequences may result if commensal organisms are destroyed by chemical treatments?

● Bacteria in the lower digestive tract restrict the growth of potentially harmful enteric organisms, provide faecal bulk and may also contribute to nutritional status (e.g. *Escherichia coli* manufacture vitamin K in the gut, which is available for the host). Antibacterial drug treatment may destroy gut flora, allowing enteric pathogens to flourish and disturbing normal digestion and absorption. Commensal bacteria (*Lactobacillus* species) growing on the surface of the vaginal epithelium may suppress the growth of the fungus *Candida albicans* by maintaining a slightly acid environment. Antibacterial treatment may allow the overgrowth of *C. albicans*, leading to thrush infections.

Achieving a satisfactory balance between elimination of pathogens and preservation of commensal microbes is a difficult problem, partly because so many variables are involved (different drugs, patients of different ages and health status, different microflora in different populations, different diets, etc.).

Protecting organisms in the environment

Organisms outside the body are also of considerable importance and, unlike those inside, they benefit from substantial legislation to protect them from inappropriate use of antimicrobial and related chemicals. Useful environmental microbes, non-pathogenic invertebrates, fish, birds and other vertebrates can all be harmed. Historically, chemical damage has often resulted from one of three causes:

*   inefficient vector control (e.g. the use of broad spectrum insecticides, or insecticides used improperly);

*   disinfectants, antiseptics and sterilizing fluids released into the environment (e.g. into hospital drains);

*   antibacterial medicines (antibiotics) or their metabolites excreted by humans or animals and entering water supplies, the food chain, etc.

Since the 1980s, in Europe, the USA and elsewhere, numerous legislative requirements concerning the release of anti-infective agents into the environment have been laid down. Individual countries and regulatory bodies within them frequently establish new regulations concerning residue limits in food, water and land; pharmaceutical companies have to collect toxicity data relating to environmental species, in addition to data relating to human toxicity. Both in Europe and the USA, data of this type have to be provided as part of the product registration process for new chemical anti-infective agents. For example, sulfonamide antibacterials are covered by 'Release into Air' controls; the disinfectant compound phenol is covered in Europe by legislation including European Commission directives on Drinking Water Concentrations and a UK Statutory Instrument relating to Release into Air, as well as routine COSHH (Control of Substances Hazardous to Health) legislation. Phenol was first used by Joseph Lister in the 1860s to prevent infection during surgery, and phenolic compounds are still commonly used as disinfectants today.

Insecticides and other pesticides used to control vectors are covered by even more environmental regulations than are medicinal drugs, but individual compounds have varied in their acceptability over time and between countries. Because of different needs and risk-benefit ratios, an insecticide may be banned from use in one country, but acceptable in another, because it provides the greatest protection at the lowest environmental cost. The most famous example is DDT, about which there are ongoing disputes between agencies that seek to ban its use on environmental grounds, and agencies that want to go on using it to save lives in heavily-infected malarial regions to control the mosquito population.

(If you are interested in detailed examples of issues and legislation pertinent to biocides, see Lippincott *et al.* (2001) under *Further Sources* at the end of this book. For examples of the type of toxicity data collected for chemicals used by the pesticide and pharmaceutical industries, see the website of the Royal Society of Chemistry (follow the links from the S320 website, under *Course Resources*).

Summary of Section 2.2

1   Anti-infective chemical agents vary in their efficacy at killing or preventing the replication of pathogenic organisms; those within the range of a particular chemical constitute its spectrum of activity, which may be broad or narrow. Efficacy varies even against organisms within a chemical's spectrum of activity.

2   Selectivity is an important factor when considering the usage of anti-infective chemicals. The concept incorporates the spectrum of activity and efficacy of a chemical against a range of target organisms, and the level of selective toxicity for non-target organisms, both within the human body and in the external environment.

3   Laboratory tests of efficacy, spectrum of activity and selective toxicity provide data to inform the setting of regulations and guidelines on conditions of use, safety levels and release into the environment. Testing regimens should ideally simulate 'real life' conditions of usage, which may affect the outcomes.

2.3 Chemical properties that combat infection

In theory there is almost infinite potential for chemical efficacy against infectious agents, but poor selectivity means that many thousands of potential anti-infective chemicals are found to be unsuitable for therapeutic use. In this section we examine some of the ways in which chemicals can inflict damage on pathogens, parasites and their vectors, and consider what factors may adversely influence their ability to do so. Even if time and space were available, it would be impossible to list all the properties of chemicals that can be harnessed to combat infection, since new properties are being identified literally on a daily basis. Here we will consider just four examples of different types of chemical property to illustrate the diverse nature of the chemical strategies that can be used to combat infectious disease.

The examples that follow vary in their clinical, social or economic importance. They include biocides and anti-infective medicines for human prescription. Notice that the activity of these agents can be based on their *physico-chemical* properties (e.g. their viscosity, their ability to attract or repel water molecules, their surface electrical charge), or on their *biochemical* properties (their ability to engage in metabolic reactions with the chemical constituents of living cells or body fluids).

2.3.1 Chemicals that alter surface tension

In the field of infection treatment and control, the physico-chemical properties of anti-infective agents are frequently overshadowed by the more intriguing biochemical properties linked to chemical reactions and bonding, but they nevertheless have a major contribution to make. One property that has been harnessed for centuries (for example, in soap) is the ability of some chemicals to alter the *surface tension* of liquids. Surface tension is a shorthand for the cohesive forces responsible for the formation of the 'skin' that enables liquid droplets to hold their shape; it also allows low-density matter to be supported on the surface of still liquids.

Chemicals that can alter the surface tension of, for example, water or fats, are known as **surfactants**. This property can be harnessed in a number of ways, several of which will be familiar to you. Detergents disrupt the surface tension of organic matter (especially fats) adhering to crockery and eating implements, and many commonly used disinfectants and household cleaning fluids reduce microbial contamination by acting as surfactants.

☐   Would you expect surfactants used in detergents, disinfectants or cleaning agents to be harmless to humans?

⬤   Although they are not normally harmful to the majority of the population when used in the correct way at recommended concentrations, allergic reactions still occur in some people. Contact with the eye or (in some cases) mucosal surfaces, such as the inside of the nose, can cause irritation. Dry flaky skin is another adverse effect of prolonged contact with even dilute solutions (e.g. after too much dishwashing with unprotected hands), because surfactants 'de-grease' the skin as well as the dishes.

A quite different application for surfactants is in the control of insect vectors that breed in still water.

○ Suggest some examples of infectious or parasitic diseases transmitted by insects that breed in water.

● Malarial parasites (*Plasmodium* species) are transmitted by *Anopheles* mosquitoes (see the *Malaria* CD-ROM associated with Book 1, Chapter 3); the virus that causes yellow fever is transmitted by the *Aedes aegyptii* mosquito (Book 2, Section 1.5.2); filarial worms, which cause lymphatic filariasis and river blindness, are transmitted by mosquitoes and blackflies (Book 2, Section 7.5.2).

In the absence of surfactants, the water surface behaves like a solid skin and is able both to support resting males and egg-laying female insects as they stand on the water, and to allow the larvae to hook onto the surface layer and hang suspended just beneath it. If the surface tension can be disturbed, the life cycle of insects that utilize the surface effect will be disrupted. Surfactant chemicals have been used to control insect larvae in still water in many parts of the world, and in the 1960s and 70s they were a major component of the WHO's malaria elimination campaigns. Numerous products have been developed for this purpose, and the chemicals used today are usually environmentally friendly and biodegradable, in contrast to the petroleum oils of the past.

Some surfactants do not dissolve in the water or become mixed within it, but form an immiscible layer, sometimes only a molecule thick, across the water surface. Although the surfactant and the water do not mix, each surfactant molecule exerts a competitive attraction for each water molecule, which reduces the ability of the water surface to act like a skin. A bonus is that these surfactants also coat the airways of the larvae (and the pupae), where they attract water; by 'wetting' the surface of the airways, the surfactant causes the larvae to asphyxiate and drown, so it has a biocidal as well as a biostatic action.

2.3.2 Chemicals that disrupt proteins indiscriminately

The ability to damage organisms with chemicals that disrupt their proteins indiscriminately is another much used approach to disinfection, antisepsis and sterilization, which has been employed empirically for about 100 years – long before the effects on protein structure were understood.

Proteins are chains of amino acids, which coil and fold around each other into a three-dimensional structure that varies depending on external conditions (e.g. of acidity, temperature, pressure). Under the conditions in which a protein is normally found 'in life', its three-dimensional shape is known as its *native conformation*. It is stabilized by covalent and hydrogen bonds between adjacent loops of the folded chain, and by the attraction and repulsion between electrical charges on different parts of the molecule. If these stabilizing forces are disrupted, the protein changes its conformation and may become unable to fulfil its normal function. If the disruption is extensive enough to prevent the protein from reverting to its native conformation, it is said to have been irreversibly *denatured*.

Chemicals that denature microbial proteins can be utilized as biocides in situations where they do not cause significant harm to the proteins of non-target organisms, including humans. The example we have chosen to focus on here is the use of alcohols as **protein denaturing agents** in hand-washing preparations to control the spread of infection within hospitals and related institutions.

The need for health care staff to 'disinfect' their hands after touching every patient was emphasized in the case study on hospital acquired infections in Book 1, Chapter 4. (Many health care workers would argue that it is appropriate to use the term 'disinfect' here, because the hands of health care staff are in effect 'tools'; an alternative would be to speak of 'achieving hand antisepsis'.) Obviously, if hand-washes are to be used at the required level of frequency, they must have a very low propensity to cause irritation leading to conditions such as eczema and dermatitis. Human skin only has a limited capacity to resist penetration by chemical compounds, especially if defensive molecules such as fatty acids are repeatedly removed during washing.

Alcohols are among the most suitable and widely used group of chemicals in hand-washes, in particular ethanol, 1-propanol and 2-propanol. Figure 2.3 gives their structural formulae, together with three other alcohols also used as biocides. Alcohols, like many other chemical biocides, have such a broad spectrum of activity that they are generally considered to be *non-specific* antimicrobials, able to act against virtually all microbes to some extent due to the multiplicity of their toxic effect mechanisms.

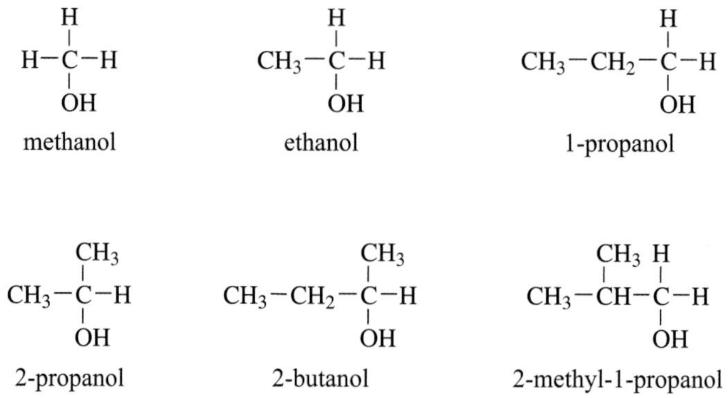

FIGURE 2.3
Structures of six alcohols with antiseptic and disinfectant properties. The stem of the name of each alcohol is determined by the number of C (carbon) atoms.

○ Describe (in simple terms) the shared features and obvious differences between the molecular structures of the alcohols illustrated in Figure 2.3.

● Each molecule only consists of carbon, hydrogen and oxygen atoms, and each possesses the characteristic C-OH group shared by all alcohols (which contributes to their similar biological actions). Some alcohols have more atoms than others (i.e. they are bigger molecules), and some have a 'straight chain' of carbon atoms leading to the –OH group, while others are branched (i.e. they have a 'side chain').

The efficacy of alcohols in damaging the function of microbes is linked to their physical properties, which vary between alcohols. Water solubility, lipophilicity (solubility in fats and hence in biological membranes), surface tension, vapour pressure, osmotic pressure and the ability to denature protein all vary with alcohol structure. Here we will only consider the predominant mode of action, which is thought to result from protein coagulation (a form of clumping together) and protein denaturation. These events occur in the microbial cell wall and the cytoplasmic membrane, but proteins found in solution within target cells and in extracellular fluids in multicellular parasites are also affected. In the case of bacteria, actions on the cell wall result in lysis of the cytoplasmic membrane and release of cellular contents, while coagulation of enzymes (all of which are proteins) leads to loss of cellular functions. With some other pathogens, alcohols can pass through outer cell membranes and act within the cells.

Not surprisingly, the efficacy of the alcohols can be influenced by a number of environmental variables. Many different alcohol-based preparations are marketed as hand-washes and it is useful to be able to compare their efficacies. Table 2.1 presents some results from such a comparison (by Kramer *et al.*, 2002), of the efficacy of hand gels (in which the active agents are applied in a jelly-like substance) and hand rinses (liquid preparations). The researchers were concerned that some hand gels might not be achieving the level of infection reduction required in European hospitals. The European Norm value EN 1500 is the standard by which hand-washes are tested under practical conditions, in comparison with an aqueous solution (60% by volume) of 2-propanol (the reference alcohol). The standard requires that the tested product should not be significantly less effective than the reference alcohol. In the test, hands were contaminated with a strain of *E. coli* and then washed with one of the gels or rinses. To establish the level of efficacy, counts of bacteria from both hands were determined pre- and post-disinfection. A mean infection reduction factor that is *less* than that of the reference alcohol indicates that a product has relatively poor efficacy in achieving hand antisepsis.

TABLE 2.1 Efficacy of alcohol-based hand antisepsis agents compared with a reference alcohol (according to the EN 1500 efficacy standard).

Brand name	Active ingredients	Mean infection reduction factor		Difference between reduction factors	*p*-value (see Box 2.6)
		product alcohol	reference alcohol		
Hand gels :					
Asanis Pro	ethanol (53%)	3.31	4.28	−0.97	<0.01
Endure 300	ethanol (70%)	2.13	4.12	−1.99	<0.01
Gel-Hydro-alcoolique	ethanol (60%)	4.09	5.07	−0.98	<0.01
Levermed Alcohol Gel	1-propanol and 2-propanol (total: 70%)	3.87	4.58	−0.71	<0.01
Manugel	2-propanol (60%) plus other antiseptics	4.07	4.96	−0.89	<0.01
Microsan	ethanol (70%)	3.36	4.26	−0.89	<0.01
Prevacare	ethanol (60%)	3.07	4.12	−1.05	<0.01
Purell	ethanol (62%)	3.07	4.10	−1.03	<0.01
Spirigel	industrial methylated spirits (70%)	3.58	4.68	−1.10	<0.01
Stokosept	ethanol (57%)	2.68	3.78	−1.10	<0.01
Hand rinses:					
AHD 2000	ethanol (75%)	4.78	4.78	0	NS
Monorapid Synergy	ethanol (54%) and 1-propanol (10%)	4.32	4.45	−0.13	NS
Softaman CH	2-propanol (45%) and 1-propanol (30%)	4.88	4.23	+0.55	NS
Sterillium	2-propanol (45%) and 1-propanol (30%) plus another antiseptic	4.26	4.10	+0.16	NS

NS = difference between efficacy of reference alcohol and test product is not statistically significant. Products are listed in alphabetical order of brand name.

> ### BOX 2.6   A note on probability values (p)
>
> The p-value is arrived at by performing a statistical test, which estimates the probability (p) that the observed differences between two results could occur by chance, if *in fact* there was no difference between them (the null hypothesis). If there is a low enough probability that chance effects could produce differences as large as those obtained (conventionally the threshold is taken to be $p < 0.05$, or 1 in 20), then the null hypothesis can be rejected and the differences in the results are held to be statistically significant. For example, if there was *no real difference* in the performance of the product alcohol and the reference alcohol in the top row of Table 2.1, then we would have to conclude that the observed difference in their reduction factors had arisen by chance. However, a statistical significance test has enabled the researchers to estimate that the probability of such a big difference in the reduction factors arising by chance is only < 0.01 (less than 1 in 100). When the probability value of chance effects producing these results is as low as < 0.01, it is conventional to conclude that the difference is *not* due to chance, and that there is a statistically significant difference between the performance of the two alcohol preparations.

○ In Table 2.1, which products were satisfactory, in that they were not significantly *worse* at reducing hand infection than the reference alcohol?

● The hand rinses were all satisfactory in comparison with the reference alcohol (the differences between them were not statistically significant). All the gels tested failed to reach the EN 1500 standard, and their lower efficacy in comparison to the reference alcohol was statistically significant in every case.

The gels and rinses were not of identical composition, so it is important to recognize that the study does not show that gels are necessarily inferior products for achieving hand antisepsis. But it does show that many hand-washing gels are inferior to some rinses under conditions of normal use, even though they contain the same alcohols in similar concentrations. Table 2.1 illustrates the influence of 'mode of delivery' on the efficacy of anti-infective chemicals.

2.3.3 Antimetabolites

We now turn our attention to anti-infective drugs, i.e. chemicals that act against pathogens inside the body. In this section, we shall look at a particular class of chemicals whose discovery represented a landmark in the field of antibacterial chemotherapy. A major breakthrough in the 1930s (prior to the development of penicillin-based antibiotics) was the discovery of antibacterial drugs that interfered with the structure and/or the function of key *metabolites* in bacterial cells. In this context, 'metabolite' refers to any chemical compound that has a role in the natural metabolism of the target microbe. (But be aware that 'metabolite' has other meanings in other contexts; for example, when discussing the way in which humans and animals modify drug molecules, the term metabolite is used to describe the *products* of such modification.) These drugs became known as **antimetabolites** and they are all *analogues* of (i.e. they structurally resemble) a natural precursor of the key bacterial metabolite whose function they disrupt.

Sulfonamides

The first antimetabolites to come into clinical use were the *sulfonamides* (the name reflects the sulfur-containing group and the amide group that characterize this class, see Figure 2.4; in the 1990s, the original spellings of 'sulphur' and 'sulphonamides' were changed in the list of British Approved Names). When sulfonamides were first developed they were highly effective against a range of bacterial infections, but although a few are still in use today, they have diminished in importance, mainly because widespread bacterial resistance has evolved. In the UK, sulfamethoxazole (in combination with an unrelated antibiotic, trimethoprim, which acts on a different point in the same metabolic pathway) is the only class member still prescribed to any significant extent. The combined drug is used to treat lung, urinary or ear infections on rare occasions, and pneumonia caused by a single-celled organism *Pneumocystis carinii*, an opportunistic pathogen with biological features mid-way between fungal and protozoal cells, usually associated with HIV infection. Despite their limited importance in modern chemotherapy, there are three reasons to discuss sulfonamides here:

- their history serves to illustrate the concept of *prodrugs*;

- their mode of action is well understood and illustrates the general category of antimetabolites;

- the basis of their selective toxicity is simple.

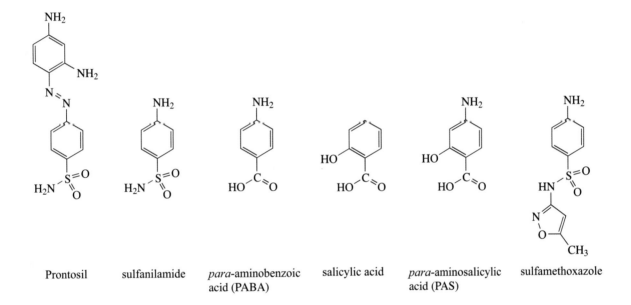

FIGURE 2.4 Structures of antibacterial compounds known collectively as the sulfonamides, which are derived from or related to sulfanilamide, with salicylic acid (the active ingredient in aspirin) for comparison. The original member of the class was the dye, Prontosil.

Prodrugs

In the 1930s, the German scientist Gerhard Domagk found the dye Prontosil (Figure 2.4) to be effective against streptococci in mice, and within two years it had become generally available as an antibacterial drug. One important feature of this compound was that although it was active *in vivo*, it was almost inactive *in vitro*. It was subsequently shown that *in vivo*, the drug was broken down to the simpler molecule *sulfanilamide* (Figure 2.4), which has the antibacterial activity. Prontosil was thus revealed to be a **prodrug** – a drug that has to be metabolized within the body before it becomes active. In this instance the discovery was a chance finding, but pharmaceutical companies have since deliberately synthesized prodrugs to extend the options available for antibacterial chemotherapy and to improve selective toxicity.

○ How might prodrugs deliver greater selective toxicity?

● Drugs must reach their target pathogens in the body, possibly inside host cells, and act against them effectively without causing significant harm to the host or commensal organisms; prodrugs may show improved selective toxicity by reaching their target *before* they are activated, so all the toxic effect is concentrated on the pathogens.

The concept has even been extended to disinfectants, where the potential for disguising biocides as nutrients is being examined. One approach has involved chemically combining a phenolic disinfectant with the sugar galactose, in such a way as to trick bacteria into responding as if only the galactose were present. The combined molecule is taken up into the bacteria, the chemical link between the components is broken by bacterial enzymes, and the biocide is released into the interior of the pathogens.

Competitive compounds

The mode of action of the sulfonamides against bacteria was found to reside in their ability to interfere with the action of a natural nutrient (*para*-aminobenzoic acid, PABA), which bacteria utilize to synthesize a key metabolic facilitator (folic acid). It was demonstrated experimentally that increasing the concentration of PABA available to bacteria reduced the effectiveness of the sulfonamides as antibacterial agents; conversely, decreasing PABA increased the efficacy of the drugs. The explanation for this effect is that PABA and the sulfonamides are **competitive compounds**, which have similar conformational structures and are competing for the same enzyme, or receptor site. The structural similarities between Prontosil, sulfanilamide and PABA can be seen clearly in Figure 2.4.

Figure 2.5 summarises some of the ways in which antibacterial chemicals interfere with various functions of their targets, including (at the bottom of the diagram) the action of sulfonamides in competition with PABA for enzymes that catalyse the synthesis of folic acid from PABA. (Trimethoprim has a similar site of action.)

FIGURE 2.5

Target sites for some antibacterial agents; notice in particular that the sulfonamides (and trimethoprim) compete with the nutrient PABA (*para*-aminobenzoic acid) for enzymes involved in synthesizing folic acid.

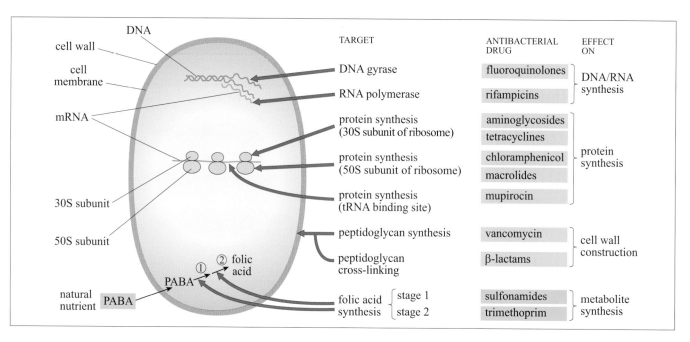

Given that folic acid is an important metabolic facilitator in human cells as well as in bacteria, you might expect that the sulfonamides would impair human metabolic functions (i.e. they would have poor selective toxicity). However, humans acquire folic acid from their diet, whereas bacteria have to make it from PABA, so we are not susceptible to agents that inhibit the synthesis of folic acid. Antimetabolite drugs that have this action are often referred to as 'folic acid antagonists'.

- ☐ Can you recall (from Book 2) which other major category of infectious agents is susceptible to folic acid antagonists?

- ⬤ Protoctists are unable to absorb folic acid from their hosts, so they have to synthesise it for themselves; competitive compounds that inhibit folic acid metabolism are important in the treatment of toxoplasmosis (see Book 2, Table 5.1 and Section 5.5.1)

The discovery and elucidation of the mode of action of the sulfanilamide molecule led subsequently to the investigation of several thousands of active molecules sharing common sulfonamide characteristics. In due course, a related chemical, *para-aminosalicylic acid* (PAS), was also found to have antimetabolite properties – and, more importantly, some selectivity for mycobacteria, including *Mycobacterium tuberculosis*. The principal mode of action of PAS is thought to be similar to that of the sulfonamides, but it has other antibacterial properties, e.g. influencing iron uptake into mycobacteria and possibly acting as an antimetabolite for salicylic acid. (For comparative purposes, Figure 2.4 includes PAS and salicylic acid.) You will learn more about antitubercular drugs (including PAS) in the *Tuberculosis* Case Study, which you will study at the end of this chapter.

2.3.4 Inhibitors of viral reverse transcriptase

As with bacteria, attempts have been made to find chemicals that can interfere with viral functions in ways that cause their destruction or prevent their replication. The last type of chemotherapeutic action that we will consider in this section is the use of *enzyme inhibitors* aimed at viral reverse transcriptase. This specific type of inhibition is one of the most intensively researched of all the chemical strategies against viral pathogens, and has been driven by the urgency of combating infection with HIV.

The nature of viral replication was discussed in Book 2, Section 3.3, and retrovirus replication was detailed in the *HIV* Case Study associated with Book 3.

- ☐ Explain how drugs that inhibit reverse transcriptase could be effective chemotherapeutic agents against retrovirus infections.

- ⬤ Retroviruses like HIV require the enzyme RNA reverse transcriptase to make a DNA copy of their RNA genome, which is then used as the template on which a complementary strand of DNA is constructed. The double-stranded DNA so formed can then be integrated into the host cell's DNA, where it instructs the synthesis of viral proteins and viral RNA and their assembly into new virus particles. Inhibition of RNA reverse transcriptase thus prevents retroviral replication within infected host cells.

Two distinct types of chemicals with this property are currently in use to slow the replication of HIV: they are the **nucleoside analogue reverse transcriptase inhibitors (NARTIs)**, and the **non-nucleoside reverse transcriptase inhibitors (NNRTIs)**.

NARTIs

Nucleosides are combinations of sugars (such as ribose or deoxyribose) and nucleic acid bases (adenosine, cytosine, guanine, thymine or uracil). They become phosphorylated within cells to form nucleotides, some of which are incorporated into DNA or RNA.

○ How might a nucleoside *analogue* interfere with retroviral replication?

● Analogues of a natural substrate (in this case a nucleoside), compete with it for the enzyme that normally acts upon that natural substrate. Thus, nucleoside analogues that compete with DNA nucleosides for binding sites on reverse transcriptase, will interfere with the transcription of the retroviral RNA genome into viral DNA.

This is how NARTIs inhibit the action of reverse transcriptase, and (just like natural nucleosides) they have to be phosphorylated within the host cell before they become effective – so in this respect, they act as prodrugs. The best known compound in this class is zidovudine (chemical name: 3'-azido-2',3'-dideoxythymidine); its structural formula is shown in Figure 2.6a, alongside that of the natural nucleoside thymidine with which it competes. Zidovudine acts as a *chain terminator* in the synthesis of DNA alongside the viral RNA template, which is catalysed by reverse transcriptase. If the drug is incorporated in place of thymidine, it prevents synthesis of the DNA chain beyond that point. The requirement for compounds like zidovudine to be phosphorylated before they can act as chain terminators means that they are inactive outside host cells.

○ Why don't NARTIs prevent the synthesis of new DNA in people who take them?

● Humans do not transcribe new DNA molecules from RNA templates, so they do not have reverse transcriptase in their cells.

However, there are a number of potentially serious side-effects of taking zidovudine and other anti-retroviral drugs (e.g. nausea, diarrhoea, headaches, anaemia), some of which result from interference with human enzymes. Problems with selective toxicity also apply to NNRTIs.

NNRTIs

In contrast to nucleoside analogues like zidovudine, NNRTIs are inhibitors that bind at or near the active site of the reverse transcriptase enzyme, and prevent it from binding to its natural substrate. The NNRTI drugs available in 2003 act by attaching themselves close to the active site of reverse transcriptase at what is described as an 'allosteric site'. This binding alters the conformation of the active site so that the enzyme cannot perform its normal function. The structural formulae for three frequently prescribed NNRTIs (nevirapine, efavirenz and delavirdine) are shown in Figure 2.6b, where it can be seen that, despite their similar actions, there is little obvious structural similarity between them.

No activation of these drugs is required, so NNRTIs can act both inside and outside host cells, making them potentially useful for incapacitating virions *before* they bind to lymphocytes and other cells for which they are tropic (i.e. able to infect). The clinical significance of the ability of NNRTIs to act outside host cells is discussed later (in Section 2.7), where we also refer to the difficulties to be overcome in designing drug molecules that can reach and penetrate infected cells.

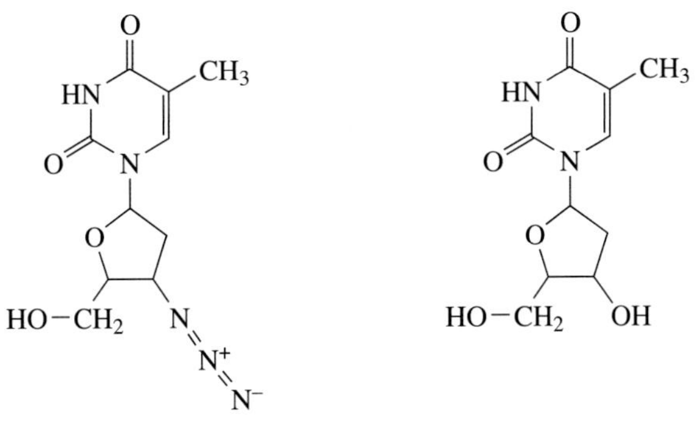

(a)   zidovudine   thymidine

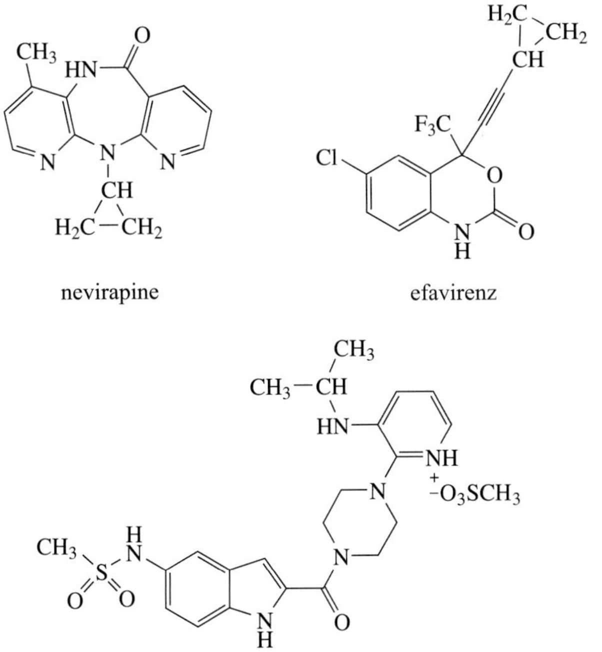

nevirapine   efavirenz

delavirdine

(b)

FIGURE 2.6
(a) The structure of zidovudine, a nucleoside analogue reverse transcriptase inhibitor (NARTI) and thymidine, the natural nucleoside with which it competes.
(b) The structures of the non-nucleoside reverse transcriptase inhibitors (NNRTIs) nevirapine, efavirenz and delavirdine.

If you want more detailed information on the modes of action of antibacterial chemicals, refer to S204 Book 4, Chapter 7, pp. 297–313 on the *Reference* CD; see also Block (2001), Maillard (2002) and McDevitt *et al.* (2002), under *Further Sources* at the end of this book. For reviews of the actions of NNRTIs and NARTIs see Davies (2000) and Jordan (2002).

Summary of Section 2.3

1   Chemicals can be used in diverse ways to combat infection either outside the body (biocides) or within the body (medicines), based on their physico-chemical and/or their biochemical properties.

2   Surfactants are used in disinfectants and cleaning agents to remove microbial contamination by disrupting the surface tension of adherent material (mainly fats). They also make an important contribution to strategies to control insect vectors that breed in still water, by disrupting the surface tension of the water.

3   The ability of chemicals to denature proteins is exploited in non-specific biocides that destroy a broad range of microbes. Alcohols are good examples of chemicals possessing this property, which is utilized in hand-washing preparations to reduce cross-infection in health care.

4   The sulfonamide drug class illustrates how antimetabolites, as analogues of naturally occurring bacterial substrates, act as competitive compounds in antibacterial chemotherapy; they also illustrate the concept of prodrugs.

5   An important contribution to anti-retroviral chemotherapy is made by drugs that inhibit the enzyme reverse transcriptase, disrupting the synthesis of viral DNA from viral RNA. These drugs are either analogues of naturally occurring nucleosides (the NARTIs), or they inhibit nucleoside binding to the enzyme active site (NNRTIs).

2.4 Influences on the efficacy of chemical agents

Although the four types of action described in Section 2.3 are very different, they are all governed by the same chemical principles. It is not surprising, therefore, that they are all susceptible to influence by a range of variables such as the concentration of the chemical agent, the exposure time, the temperature and acidity of the local environment, and the presence (or absence) of water or other chemicals. For each of these variables there is sometimes an optimum value, such as an ideal temperature at which the efficacy of a chemical agent is at its maximum. However, as you will see in what follows, it is not necessarily the case that 'more is better'; for example, you cannot assume that the greater the concentration, the more effective a chemical will be.

2.4.1 Concentration, exposure time and local conditions

The variables of concentration, exposure time and local conditions apply to actions of chemicals both inside and outside the body. However, the influence of these variables can be illustrated more simply for biocides acting outside the body, so we return to the actions of alcohols to provide an example. It has been known for many years that, in the absence of water, proteins are not denatured by 'pure' (i.e. 100%) alcohols as readily as when water is present. You may be surprised to discover that pure ethanol (absolute ethanol) can be *less* bactericidal than mixtures of ethanol and water.

Table 2.2 (adapted from Smith, 1947) shows results obtained over 50 years ago in studies assessing the efficacy of ethanol against *Mycobacterium tuberculosis* in the environment. These results simultaneously illustrate the effects of three variables: concentration, exposure time and the local environment of the organisms. The index of efficacy used in these studies was the time needed to kill all the bacteria, and from this it is implicit that the effectiveness of an anti-infective agent in killing or damaging a target microbe is linked to the duration of exposure.

○   What evidence does Table 2.2 provide to support the assertion that – in the absence of water – bacterial proteins are not denatured by alcohols as readily as when water is present?

●   Table 2.2 (adapted from Smith, 1947) shows that the efficacy of 100% ethanol, using wet sputum as the infective source, was *less* than that obtained with 95% ethanol and no more effective than 70% ethanol. Applied to a thick layer of dried sputum, both 100% and 95% solutions were much less effective than 70%, and 100% took more than twice as long as 95% to achieve the same effect.

TABLE 2.2 Tuberculocidal effect of ethanol under various conditions.

Condition of treated specimen:	Tuberculocidal exposure	
	Ethanol concentration (as % of volume)	Time taken to kill all *M. tuberculosis*
in sputum (wet)	100	30 seconds
	95	15 seconds
	70	30 seconds
	50	60 seconds
in water	100	30 seconds
	95	15 seconds
	70	60 seconds
in sputum (dried):		
thin layer	70	60 seconds
	50	60 seconds
thick layer	100	>60 minutes
	95	30 minutes
	70	5–10 minutes

Clearly, this type of information on concentration, exposure time and local conditions is not only of theoretical interest, but also of practical relevance to hospitals, clinics, laboratories and even domestic situations. For example, it is common practice to swab skin with an antiseptic solution (usually containing an alcohol) prior to giving injections. Although this may physically remove dirt and debris from the skin, it is very doubtful whether the exposure time before the injection is given is sufficient to kill any microbes present on the skin. Likewise, when disinfectant sprays or solutions are used to clean surfaces domestically, it is doubtful whether sufficient time is allowed for true disinfection (which may take hours to achieve), even if the chemical agent is capable of producing it. The same problem can occur in health care settings, where systematic monitoring and modification of inadequate procedures should be in place to ensure that effective disinfection is achieved. However, the extent of hospital acquired infections (Book 1, Chapter 4) suggests that procedures are not always successful.

2.4.2 Influence of pH

One of the most important factors influencing the action of anti-infective agents is the pH (see Box 2.7 overleaf) of the environments they encounter during use. You will probably be aware that many molecules or parts of molecules alter their electrical state depending on the pH of their environment. Easily identified extremes are when an atom or molecule exists as either a negatively or a positively charged *ion*, or in a totally non-ionized (uncharged) state. It also often occurs that one part of a molecule is positively charged and another is negatively charged (e.g. zidovudine and delarvidine, Figure 2.6). Any of these states may apply both to the chemical constituents of the infecting organism and to the anti-infective agent.

> ## BOX 2.7   A note on pH
>
> The pH of an aqueous (water-based) solution is a measure of its acidity – the lower the pH, the more acid the solution. The pH scale is based on the concentration of positively charged hydrogen ions (H^+) in the solution; pH 7.0 is considered to be 'neutral' and solutions with values above 7.0 are traditionally referred to as 'alkaline', although in modern chemistry they are simply less acid points on a continuous scale. The so-called 'physiological pH' for human tissues is 7.4 and most biochemical reactions in human cells occur with maximum efficiency at this pH. If the pH of a solution rises or falls, then the electrical charges on any molecules dissolved in it may change, previously uncharged molecules may become ionized, and these changes in electrical conformation may alter the activity of the molecule.

Values of pH influence the actions of anti-infective chemicals in two separate ways. Firstly, infectious organisms usually function optimally at a particular pH, thus any alteration to this pH can reduce their ability to grow and multiply, which in turn may increase the efficacy of agents used against them. Secondly, the efficacy of a chemical can alter with changes in local pH, as a consequence of changes in its electrical conformation. Many biocides, for example, need to be at least partially ionized in order to be effective and they may only achieve this state within a relatively narrow range of pH values; thus efficacy needs to be tested across the range of pHs at which the biocide may have to act.

Though critically important, it is relatively straightforward to match the right biocide with a particular environment. However, the issues are much more complex for chemicals used within the body, because the molecules must have the right characteristics both to reach their target site and to be active when they get there. Specific uptake mechanisms can transport ionized molecules into cells, but in general, molecules in a non-ionized state can penetrate microbial membranes and host cells more readily than ionized molecules can do. Thus, at least the key parts of many anti-infective drugs used in human chemotherapy must be in a non-ionized state at the physiological pH of 7.4 in order to be able to reach their targets.

◯ What pH conditions of importance would an orally active drug targeting a lung infection encounter after its ingestion?

⬤ The drug would first experience the acid environment of the stomach. Assuming it is not totally absorbed at this site, it will then experience the alkaline environment of the small intestine. Outside the gut, and in the vicinity of the infecting organisms in the lungs, the environment will be at the physiological pH. Unless the drug utilizes carrier-mediated transport to penetrate host or microbial cells, it will need to be at least partially non-ionized at the pH of the stomach or the intestine, and at physiological pH.

In the next section of this chapter, we consider an overview of where, when and how chemicals can be used to combat infection, bearing in mind the influences on their efficacy that we have just discussed. Then, in Section 2.6, we take this discussion into an area of greater complexity by illustrating the influence of individual differences in physiology on the efficacy of a drug acting within the body.

Summary of Section 2.4

1   Several factors influence the efficacy of anti-infective agents and among the most important are concentration, exposure time and local conditions (including pH).

2   For some chemical agents, there may be a relatively narrow optimum range (e.g. of temperature, water content, pH) at which their action against pathogenic microbes reaches maximum efficacy.

3   Many biocides have to be in a partially ionized state to be effective disinfectants. By contrast, in the absence of specific uptake mechanisms, chemotherapeutic agents are generally more able to enter target or host cells if they are in a non-ionized state than when they carry an electrical charge.

2.5 An overview of chemical strategies

In this short section we review the chemical strategies we have discussed so far and locate them in an overall model of 'where, when and how' chemicals can be used to combat infection (see Figure 2.7 overleaf). There is insufficient time and space to consider all the types of intervention in Figure 2.7, but some of the uses will already be familiar to you and others will be discussed later in the chapter. Note that although we are focusing on human infectious disease in this course, chemicals are also used in all of these ways to combat infection in other species, particularly those that provide food crops and domestic livestock.

The left side of Figure 2.7 concentrates on ways in which anti-infective chemicals can be used *prior* to significant exposure of an individual to infecting organisms. The term 'significant' in this context indicates an exposure sufficient for some harmful consequence to result. One strategic aim of chemical interventions prior to significant exposure is to reduce the 'counts' of harmful organisms *outside* the body in locations where they pose a threat to humans.

○   Give an example of a chemical intervention discussed earlier in the chapter for each of the three pink 'boxes' on the left side of Figure 2.7.

◓   Biocides that reduce counts of harmful organisms in the external environment on surfaces, tools, etc., include phenol and other disinfectants, and alcohols in antiseptic hand-washes reduce cross-infection (e.g. in the catering industry, clinical settings, domestic environments). Surfactants can be used to control some insect vectors by disrupting the surface tension of the still water in which they breed. Preservatives can be added to water, medicines and food to prevent the growth of contaminating organisms.

Chemicals can also be used outside the body to control vectors in novel ways, for example, to combat sleeping sickness in Eastern Africa. In this region, the *Trypanosoma* parasites are transmitted by savannah-dwelling tsetse flies (*Glossina* species), which take infected blood meals from large grazing mammals such as cows, antelope and zebra, and also bite humans. Traps baited with chemicals that reproduce the odour of cow breath and cow urine are very successfully used to attract the flies, which are killed by the insecticides with which the traps are also impregnated!

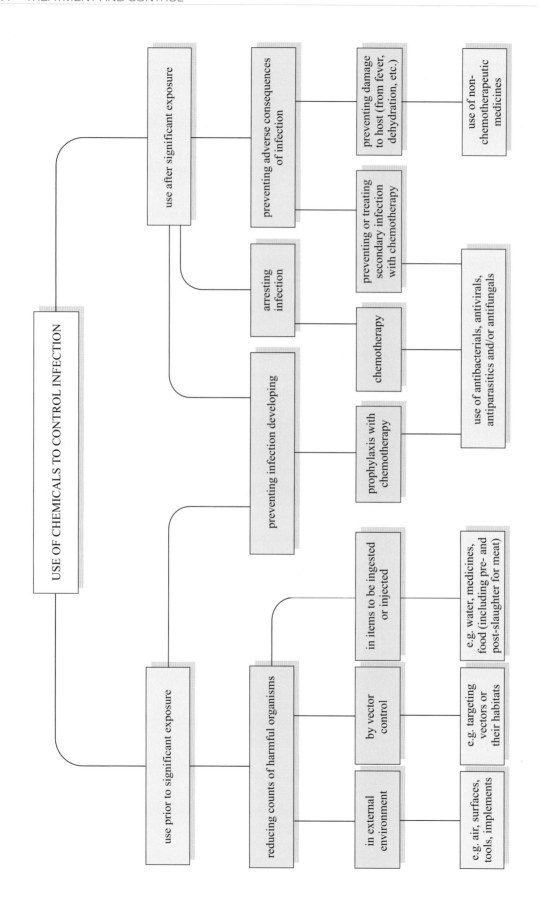

FIGURE 2.7   An overview of where, when and how chemicals can be used to prevent, treat or control infection. (Note: you will need to look at this diagram again when you study Section 6 of the *Tuberculosis* Case Study later in this chapter.)

In the rest of this chapter, we focus on chemicals that act *inside* the body. The right side of Figure 2.7 concentrates on use of chemicals *after* a significant exposure, and deals with ways of minimizing the effects of infection with drugs, usually, but not always, targeting the infective organism.

○ In the centre of Figure 2.7 are scenarios involving *prophylactic* chemotherapy. Suggest an example of a situation in which drugs might be prescribed *after* a known exposure to prevent infection from developing and an example of drug use *prior* to an expected exposure.

● You may have suggested different examples, but reverse transcriptase inhibitors are given to people who have been accidentally exposed to HIV, for example, as a result of a 'needle-stick' injury to a health worker caring for someone with AIDS. Individuals may be prescribed preventive drugs when travelling to a region where a particular infectious or parasitic disease is endemic and for which there is no vaccine; antimalarial drugs are the most obvious example.

To highlight the main strategic issues involved in the use of post-infection and prophylactic treatments in humans, we will discuss examples of chemical interventions with the following aims:

• arresting a simple primary infection with antibacterial drugs, using syphilis to introduce the important concept of *pharmacokinetics* (Section 2.6);

• arresting an infection with multiple drug therapy, using a range of examples including HIV and TB (Section 2.7 and the *Tuberculosis* Case Study);

• prophylactic chemotherapy to reduce the risk of infection, using antimalarial drugs to illustrate the general principles (Section 2.8);

• preventing or treating the adverse consequences of infection, focusing on respiratory infections and diarrhoeal diseases (Section 2.9).

You are not required to learn the details of the individual drugs mentioned in the rest of this chapter, but you should make sure you understand how the information in Sections 2.6–2.9 illustrates different strategies behind the use of anti-infective chemicals.

Summary of Section 2.5

1   A model of where, when and how anti-infective chemicals are used can provide a framework for considering specific examples.

2   In the external environment, chemical intervention acts prior to significant exposure, to reduce the counts of harmful organisms or their vectors, and to prevent or reduce contamination of objects, surfaces, foods, medicines, air and water.

3   Within the body, anti-infectives may be used prophylactically, or to arrest an infection, or to prevent serious medical consequences of infection.

2.6 Arresting a primary bacterial infection

Antibacterial drugs are prescribed around the world hundreds of thousands of times each day to arrest a *primary* bacterial infection, that is, one in which the symptoms are 'primarily' attributed to infection with a particular pathogen (or general class of pathogen), rather than to multiple concurrent infections. Such illnesses are also sometimes referred to as *simple* infections, implying that the causative agent presents a relatively susceptible target for chemical intervention. To illustrate some of the key therapeutic issues involved in even this apparently straightforward type of treatment, we must introduce the concept of *pharmacokinetics*, before briefly considering a specific example – the antibacterial treatment of syphilis.

2.6.1 Pharmacokinetics

☐ In the light of discussions in earlier sections of this chapter, what criteria of efficacy and safety should an antibacterial drug be able to fulfil?

⬤ The following considerations should inform drug selection:

*   it must be effective against the target pathogen and have acceptably low selective toxicity against host cells and commensal organisms;
*   any excreted residue or breakdown products should not be toxic to organisms in the environment;
*   it should be formulated in an appropriate dosing form (e.g. a solution for injection, a tablet or capsule, or a liquid suspension for swallowing) to deliver an effective dose of active ingredient by the most effective route;
*   an appropriate concentration of active drug should be able to reach the target organisms wherever they are located in the body;
*   the dosage should be maintained at an appropriate concentration for a duration sufficient to ensure effective action against the targets (i.e. it should not be broken down too quickly).

The route of administration, the dose and the dosage regimen (the intervals between doses, the duration of treatment, etc.) are influenced by the **pharmacokinetics** of the active ingredient. This term refers to the way the drug recipient's body absorbs, distributes, metabolizes (breaks down) and excretes the active ingredient. The manufacturers of licensed medicines have to address the pharmacokinetic issues by establishing the absorption, distribution and elimination characteristics of the drug through extensive laboratory research and clinical trials. They design a formulation suitable for the drug's characteristics, determine appropriate dosage ranges, check for metabolic interactions with other drugs, and present convincing evidence on all these (and other safety and efficacy considerations) to the licensing authorities, before the drug can be prescribed for clinical use.

However, even when a drug has been licensed, the prescriber also has to take into account the individual characteristics of the person for whom it is being prescribed. Consideration of pharmacokinetics is especially important for certain categories of patient, for example, pregnant women or infants. In pregnancy, the extent to which the foetus is exposed to the drug has to be taken into account, and doses for infants have to be adjusted to their low body-weight and relatively poor ability to eliminate chemicals.

○ In what other groups of patients would you expect pharmacokinetic considerations to be especially important in drug prescription?

● They include elderly, obese or malnourished people, those with digestive, liver or kidney disorders, and people with dependencies on other drugs (e.g. alcohol), all of whom may not be able to absorb, distribute or eliminate the drug as efficiently as someone without these characteristics.

Another important category is individuals with psychological, psychiatric or behavioural problems, who may not be able to cope with the challenge of taking their medicine in the correct dosage regimen for the prescribed period.

○ How might the patient's immunological status influence the choice of an antibacterial drug to treat an infection?

● Allergies to antibacterial drugs (e.g. penicillin) are fairly common and prescribers often question patients concerning any history of drug-related hypersensitivity. Manifestations can range from a slight rash to a life-threatening systemic inflammatory reaction (anaphylaxis).

So, having outlined the key pharmacokinetic issues, how are they addressed and by whom? In a modern well-organised health service, several groups of people help to ensure that a patient taking a prescription drug is properly treated. The pharmaceutical manufacturer has to ensure that their medicinal product has the potential to treat the patient effectively, while the prescriber has to choose the correct dose, formulation and dosage regimen to meet the patient's needs. A pharmacist dispenses the medicine correctly, clearly labelled with the dosage regimen, and the patient (or a carer) has to administer the medicine as directed. If any of these four contributors fails to play their part properly, a successful outcome from the intended therapy will be at risk – a situation that occurs with alarming frequency all over the world, including medically 'advanced' countries.

2.6.2 Treating syphilis

> The background to this discussion is in the *Syphilis* Case Study and its associated television programme, to which you were referred in Book 2.

Syphilis is universally recognized as an infection for which a number of effective antibacterial drugs can be prescribed. Antibacterial therapy for most simple primary infections is prescribed on the basis of a clinical assessment of symptoms, from which a presumptive clinical diagnosis is reached. In the case of syphilis, however, many countries operate guidelines that advise laboratory confirmation for suspected cases. Here we shall assume that a positive laboratory diagnosis of infection with *Treponema pallidum* has been made, that the infection is in the early stages, and that there is no significant concurrent infection with another pathogenic organism. For simplicity, we shall also assume our example patient is an able-bodied adult male suffering from no other medical or psychological disorder.

In the UK, antibacterial therapy for such a patient is straightforward: the recommended licensed treatment is a 14-day course of either doxycycline or erythromycin. There is little to choose between the two drugs in terms of efficacy and both are prescribed as oral formulations for treatment of early syphilis. Doctors can also prescribe procaine benzylpenicillin as a 10-day treatment by intramuscular injection, but (in 2003) this does not have a product license for use as an antisyphilitic agent in the UK. In other countries (such as the USA), different treatment regimens are preferred, for example a single large dose by intramuscular injection of benzathine penicillin, in situations where regular or daily medication may be difficult to ensure.

Summary of Section 2.6

The decision on what medicine to prescribe and what dosage to administer, even for a simple primary bacterial infection, is based on:

1   the nature of the infecting organism;

2   the availability of an effective medicine in an appropriate formulation;

3   the pharmacokinetics of the active ingredient and the influence of the patient's characteristics (e.g. age, pregnancy, etc.) on the absorption, distribution and elimination of the drug;

4   the presence of any concurrent conditions (e.g. other infections, immunodeficiency, psychiatric problems, alcohol dependency, liver damage, kidney damage, etc.).

2.7 Arresting infection with multiple therapy

> Multiple-drug therapy is required to treat tuberculosis effectively. At a convenient point in the study period remaining for this chapter, and before progressing to Chapter 3, you should turn to Section 6 of the *Tuberculosis* Case Study and the tutorial entitled 'Treatment' on the accompanying *Tuberculosis* CD, where you will find material on chemical interventions for TB. You should allow about one hour to study this material.

A rule of thumb for all therapy with medicinal drugs is that, whenever possible, it is better to use a single therapy for treatment of a single medical problem.

▢   What advantages do you see in this approach?

◉   It has many benefits, including: reducing the risk of adverse side effects, avoiding interactions that can occur if several drugs are taken together, a simpler dosage schedule for the patient, and lowering the drug-related 'metabolic burden' for the patient. (Although humans are generally able to inactivate the chemical compounds in prescription medicines, the systems that metabolize drugs can be impaired in a person who is ill.)

There are times however, for both non-infectious and infectious diseases, where the 'single therapy' rule has to be broken. Infectious diseases tend to require **multiple therapy** (the use of two or more drugs to treat a single infection – also known as *combination therapy* or *multi-drug therapy*) in the following circumstances:

•   when resistance to an anti-infective chemical is, or is likely to be, a problem;

•   when the most effective dose of a single anti-infective is too toxic to the patient;

•   when two or more chemicals given together act *synergistically* (i.e. the combined effect is greater than the sum of each treatment given separately);

- when the infection is life threatening and there is no time to identify the infecting organism;

- when inclusion of an *immunostimulant* in the therapy will significantly aid recovery because it boosts the host's own immune system.

It should be acknowledged that successful drug combinations have often been found by trial and error, and a complete explanation for their success is not always understood at the time and sometimes not even after further investigation. Furthermore, even when the actions of the anti-infectives are well understood, multiple therapy may be used for more than one of the reasons given above. Here, we discuss examples of well understood multiple therapy regimens to treat a range of common conditions.

2.7.1 Beta-lactamase inhibitors

The penicillins, the first 'antibiotics' to be used widely, include in their chemical structure, a *beta-lactam ring*, which is essential to their efficacy against bacterial targets. Several other antibiotics (cephalosporins, monobactams and carbapenems) also include this ring. (If you wish to view these structures, you can do so on the *Reference* CD-ROM, S204 Book 4, Chapter 7, Figure 7.6 on p. 304. The chapter also gives more details of penicillins.) However, following the widespread use of these drugs, many strains of previously susceptible bacteria evolved the ability to synthesis an enzyme, *beta-lactamase* (also known as *penicillinase*), which destroys the ring. As a consequence, these drugs are no longer effective antibacterial agents against such organisms. The problem can be overcome by co-administering a chemical that inhibits beta-lactamase and so prevents the bacteria from destroying the antibiotic. Beta-lactamase inhibitors (such as clavulanic acid) can successfully be included with beta-lactam antibiotics in an appropriate formulation to overcome this form of resistance. The two chemicals are combined in the product co-amoxiclav (better known by its brand name Augmentin).

2.7.2 Immunostimulants

Another class of therapeutic chemicals that can aid the action of traditional anti-infective drugs is the *immunostimulants*. The use of these drugs is more correctly described as 'adjunctive' therapy rather than combination therapy, because they act indirectly to promote an effective immune response against infectious agents (the use of adjuvants was introduced in Book 3, at the end of Section 2.9, and is discussed further in Chapter 3 of this book). Immunostimulants are increasing in importance, but are not yet in widespread use. They are beginning to be prescribed to some cancer patients undergoing cancer chemotherapy, which suppresses the activity of their immune system and leaves them vulnerable to opportunistic infections. Immunostimulants can enhance the production of new white cells (leukocytes) in these patients, restoring the function of the immune system more quickly and improving the ability to fight infection. The immunostimulant is generally given alongside prophylactic anti-infective therapy to protect the patient from infection during cancer treatment and in the recovery period.

2.7.3 Multiple therapy for HIV infections

> The background to this section can be found in the 'HIV' mini-lecture on *Immunology Interactive* CD2, which you studied in association with Book 3. Figure 2.8 (below) has been adapted from a screen on CD2.

In the 1990s, the most widely discussed target for multiple anti-infective therapy has been HIV, using an approach known as **highly active antiretroviral therapy (HAART)**. Figure 2.8 illustrates the sites of action of the main classes of anti-HIV drugs in current use in 2003. The most important classes of drug currently are the two types of reverse transcriptase inhibitors – NARTIs and NNRTIs (Section 2.3.4), which prevent the virus from making a DNA copy of its own viral RNA – and the *protease inhibitors*, which prevent the manufacture of essential proteins for virus replication. Two other classes of anti-HIV drugs are in development: the *fusion inhibitors*, which act by blocking the final stage of entry of the HIV particle into CD4-positive T cells (the first of these, enfuvirtide, was licensed in 2003), and the *integrase inhibitors*, which interfere with the integration of the viral genome into the host cell's DNA (no drugs in this class had been licensed in the UK by 2003).

In the early days of HIV treatment, many patients were given one drug at a time and the virus quickly developed resistance to each. The virus mutates so quickly that only

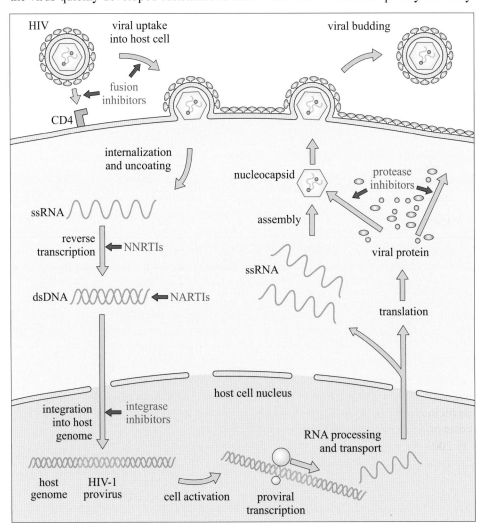

FIGURE 2.8
Sites of action of antiretroviral drugs used in HIV chemotherapy. Drug regimens typically contain combinations of drugs directed at different targets. NARTIs are nucleoside analogue reverse transcriptase inhibitors; NNRTIs are non-nucleoside reverse transcriptase inhibitors. Note that viral RNA is single stranded (ssRNA) and is reverse transcribed into double stranded DNA (dsDNA).

by using a combination of treatments can the evolution of drug resistance be controlled. Since the early 1990s, two or more antiretroviral agents have been prescribed simultaneously in HAART regimens to curb the replication of HIV in infected people. In 2003, the recommended regimen in the UK is to begin treatment with two NARTIs, plus a third agent – a protease inhibitor, a NNRTI, or another NARTI; two protease inhibitors are sometimes prescribed, making a total of four drugs.

To a large extent, the characteristics of the patient determine the choice of HAART regimen, but the need to overcome drug resistance is the main reason for using multiple therapy. By 2002, in some cities in Western Europe and the USA with relatively high incidence of HIV transmission, more than 20% of all new cases were caused by HIV strains with some resistance to at least one of the major classes of antiretroviral drugs (CIDPC Canada, 2002). In the short term, people who are infected with a drug-resistant HIV strain can generally be treated by switching to a different drug regimen. But as the spectrum of resistance increases, it is likely that **multi-drug resistant strains** (**MDRs**) will evolve, for which there are no effective treatments. This outcome is made more likely by 'cross-resistance' which occurs when a mutant virus resistant to one drug is found to be resistant to several, gradually eroding the benefit of multiple therapy with existing drugs.

A further problem with HAART regimens is the sheer number of medicines that may have to be taken – on average, around 15 tablets or capsules to be ingested per day – in a complex sequence in which some drugs must be taken with or soon after food, and others on an empty stomach. Not only does this place considerable restrictions on the patient's daily life, which some have been unable to sustain, but continuance of the treatment can also be eroded by the side effects that certain drugs can produce in some individuals (for example, body fat often redistributes to the belly, breasts and upper back, while the face and limbs become 'wasted'). The biochemical basis of the various side effects are not fully understood, but some patients have been unable to tolerate them and have chosen to abandon treatment, while others have found well-tolerated drug combinations that keep HIV counts low for a sustained period. (Issues of *compliance* with treatment for other infectious diseases are discussed further in Section 2.8 and in the *Tuberculosis* Case Study.)

Comparisons between HIV treatment regimens are difficult, because the necessary data take several years to collect and development of drug-resistance can easily overtake the findings of recently published research. Nevertheless an extensive comparative review of the different treatment regimens has concluded that the triple therapy described above tends to be the best approach to HIV treatment (Jordan *et al.*, 2002). However, there is disagreement about when treatment should begin (some experts advocate beginning HAART as soon as HIV infection is diagnosed, and others recommend waiting until HIV levels rise), and also about whether the drug regimen should be switched regularly or changed only if resistance develops.

Antiretroviral drugs are also very expensive and therefore out of reach for the vast majority of infected people worldwide. Controversy over the pricing of these medicines in the late 1990s led to various pharmaceutical companies reducing the costs or donating supplies to developing countries with high rates of HIV infection. By 2003, the cost of a year's supply of HAART drugs had fallen from several thousand dollars per person to about US$400 in India and parts of Africa – but this amount still far exceeds the capacity of individuals and government health budgets. We return to the economic and political influences on the accessibility of anti-infective agents in the final section of this chapter.

2.7.4 Multiple therapy for skin infections

Finally, it is worth mentioning a commonplace example of two or more anti-infective agents being prescribed because of their synergistic action. Several active chemical ingredients are generally included in preparations for the treatment of minor skin infections. For example, two topical fungicides can be found in some preparations to treat *Tinea* infections, such as those responsible for athlete's foot (*topical* in this context means applied to a surface, in this case the skin).

Summary of Section 2.7

1   Multiple therapy can overcome some problems of drug-resistance (as in the addition of beta-lactamase inhibitors to beta-lactam antibiotics), compensate for the unacceptable toxicity of single anti-infective agents, or act as the first resort when an unidentified pathogen is producing a life-threatening infection.

2   Immunostimulants may be included in conventional anti-infective therapy to aid recovery or protect against opportunistic infection by boosting the patient's immune response, for example during cancer chemotherapy.

3   Two or more chemicals given together may act synergistically, for example in topical preparations to treat skin infections.

4   Problems associated with multiple therapy can include the additional cost of treatments, adverse drug interactions or side-effects and the complexity of dosing regimens which may impact on patient compliance. These difficulties are exemplified by HAART regimens for HIV infection.

2.8 Prophylactic chemotherapy

As we noted in Section 2.1, prophylaxis is therapy used to prevent the development of disease or an adverse event associated with it. There are numerous instances where the use of preventive drugs as **prophylactic chemotherapy** is indicated for infection control, with a similar purpose to vaccination. However, unlike vaccination where the aim is to protect everyone in a population, prophylactic drugs are usually offered only to those judged to be particularly vulnerable to infection and then only for the duration of potential exposure to risk.

2.8.1 Individuals whose health is compromised

With a few important exceptions, prophylactic chemotherapy is most commonly advised for individuals whose health is (or is likely to become) compromised. In these circumstances, prophylactic treatment may occur, for example:

*   prior to 'dirty' surgery;
*   prior to minor surgical procedures (e.g. dental extractions) in patients with heart valve disease;
*   prior to and during recovery from organ transplantation;
*   in association with cancer therapy;
*   in people with cystic fibrosis;
*   in HIV-infected pregnant women prior to the birth of the child.

We expand briefly on each of these examples in turn. In medical parlance, 'dirty' surgery generally refers to operations that open the abdominal cavity, particularly if incisions are made in the gastrointestinal tract. Antimicrobial drugs are used prophylactically to protect the patient against wound infection and bacteraemia (blood stream infection) by gut bacteria. Typically, two antibacterials are used concurrently, one active against aerobic and one active against anaerobic organisms.

Minor procedures such as dental extractions often necessitate prophylactic treatment in patients with heart valve disease. Most individuals can cope with exposure to some infectious agents without difficulty, but valve tissue in these patients is especially vulnerable to localized infection reaching it in the bloodstream.

Several groups of immunocompromised patients may require prophylactic anti-infective chemotherapy, most commonly those receiving transplanted organs or undergoing cancer treatments. The immune system of both these groups of patients is suppressed as a consequence of the treatment they are receiving (e.g. with drugs or radiation), and it may be necessary to protect them from infection by opportunistic microbes that they would normally resist. Another reason for prophylactic treatment in these patients is to reduce the risk of drug-resistant strains of bacteria developing in hospitals.

○ Explain the rationale for this use of prophylactic chemotherapy.

● Several factors are involved. Firstly, the patient's immune system is unable to respond effectively to bacterial infection, so microbes in the environment may be able to replicate freely in the patient's body. The unrestricted proliferation in an immunocompromised host means that there are many cell divisions at which new mutants may arise with some resistance to common antibacterial drugs. Secondly, patients requiring cancer treatment or organ transplantation often have repeated and long stays in hospital, exposing them to bacteria with some degree of drug resistance, which may then evolve greater resistance in such an 'ideal' host. Thirdly, patients in these categories may need prophylactic antibacterial treatment for months or even years, so there is a long time period over which resistant bacteria are exposed to the selection pressure of antibacterial drugs.

Another group of patients who are particularly vulnerable to infection are those with cystic fibrosis. This condition, amongst other problems, impairs lung function and leaves the person highly susceptible to *Pseudomonas* infections. People with cystic fibrosis usually require lifelong prophylaxis against this and other respiratory tract infections.

One of the highest profile examples of chemoprophylaxis relates to HIV and the prevention of **mother-to-child transmission** (often abbreviated to MTCT in public health sources). Around 30% of babies born to HIV-positive mothers are themselves infected if no prophylaxis is given. In countries where a high percentage of pregnant women are HIV-positive (around 25% in South Africa in 2002), the need for effective prophylaxis is huge (see Figure 2.9 overleaf). Prophylactic use of a *single* dose of an NNRTI drug such as nevirapine injected into the mother during labour, followed by another dose for the baby within 72 hours of delivery, can reduce HIV transmission rates to <5%. (Note that some babies protected in this way are subsequently infected via their mother's breast milk.)

FIGURE 2.9
If women who test positive at antenatal clinics in areas of high HIV prevalence (as here in the West African Republic of the Gambia) can receive a single injection of an anti-retroviral drug (usually nevirapine) when they are in labour, and if their newborn babies are also treated within 72 hours, the mother-to-child transmission of HIV can be prevented in around 95% of cases.

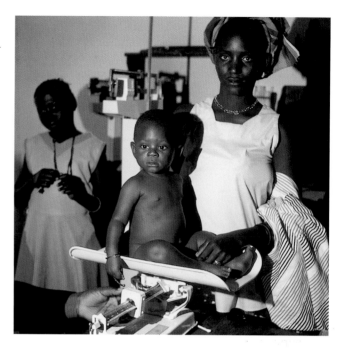

Prophylactic treatment of people in good health after known or suspected exposure to life-threatening organisms provide some of the most dramatic examples of chemoprophylaxis. For example, antiretroviral drugs are given following 'needle-stick' injuries sustained by health workers who have been accidentally punctured with a needle or other sharp object contaminated with HIV. Drugs belonging to the NNRTI class appear to offer the best chance of protection in such cases.

- ○ Suggest examples when antibacterial drugs might be prescribed to healthy people.

- ● Close contacts of individuals newly diagnosed as having meningococcal infections or tuberculosis, and the sexual partners of people with syphilis, gonorrhoea or other sexually transmitted bacterial infections, are given a course of antibacterial chemotherapy to reduce the risk that any pathogens to which they have been exposed could replicate and result in disease.

In the final part of this section, we discuss one of the most ancient uses of prophylactic chemotherapy.

2.8.2 Individuals in high-risk situations: malaria

We can now move on to the use of prophylactic drugs in individuals who are not vulnerable because of their health status, but due to their activities; for example, people travelling to an area where malaria is endemic, from one where it is not. Of course, the local population is at far greater risk from malaria, but they could not take prophylactic medicines throughout their lives (even if the drugs were available) because the side-effects of the drugs get worse over time. However, chemoprophylaxis is strongly recommended during pregnancy.

The use of chemicals for vector control to reduce the spread of malaria has already been mentioned, and although this is a preventative measure, it is not normally described as chemoprophylaxis. Antimalarial drugs used prophylactically aim to prevent the development of infection in individuals who are bitten by malaria-carrying mosquitoes. The problem is one that has plagued travellers for centuries, and even today approximately 1500 travellers from the UK contract malaria outside the country each year, and about 15 deaths occur as a result.

From your study of the *Malaria* CD-ROM (associated with Book 1, Chapter 3), you will remember that there are four species of malarial parasite. Unfortunately, they do not display identical susceptibilities to drug treatment, and furthermore, the prophylactic treatments that do exist cannot offer complete protection and must be used in association with bite-avoidance measures.

One of the most important of the groups of antimalarials is the quinoline group, typified by the synthetic drugs chloroquine (see Figure 2.10), mefloquine and the naturally occurring quinine. This group has activity only during the stages of the parasite's life cycle that occur in human red blood cells. Despite their long established use, their mode of action is still somewhat unclear. They may act by inhibiting the enzyme haem-polymerase, which is present in some parasite stages and normally detoxifies free haem, a breakdown product of human haemoglobin that would otherwise be toxic to the parasite.

FIGURE 2.10
Drugs based on chloroquine are the mainstay of chemoprophylaxis and treatment for malaria in endemic regions. Pharmaceutical companies may produce antimalarial drugs relatively cheaply for local use, as in this factory in Kampala, Uganda, photographed in 2001.

Other antimalarials are active by virtue of being inhibitors of dihydrofolate. Malarial parasites cannot take up folic acid from their environment but have to synthesise it intracellularly. If the key enzyme is inhibited, then synthesis cannot occur. Compounds falling into this class include proguanil, pyrimethamine, sulphadoxine and dapsone. Like the quinolones, these drugs act on the red cell stage, but also have some additional effects on the liver stage of the parasite's development. Ultimately, the choice of drug will depend on a variety of issues, summarized in Table 2.3 overleaf (adapted from Goodyer, 2000).

TABLE 2.3 Factors influencing the choice of antimalarial drug.

Details of itinerary
time of year
countries/areas
rural/urban
accommodation
activities planned
style of travel (business or backpack)
Travellers' details
age
pregnancy/breastfeeding
previous exposures and reactions to antimalarial drugs
previous medical history (fits, drug reactions, psychiatric illness, psoriasis)
family history (epilepsy, psychiatric illness)

As Table 2.3 suggests, several problems beset the prophylactic use of antimalarial drugs. Not only is their efficacy less than ideal, but the development of drug-resistance, especially by *Plasmodium falciparum* – the species with the highest fatality rate – is an increasing problem. In addition, there are adverse drug reactions to consider. For most antimalarials, side effects generally take the form of relatively minor gastrointestinal upsets. However, one of the most effective drugs (mefloquine) produces dizziness in a significant proportion of people and neuropsychiatric disturbances in a minority. In a few cases, severe symptoms of anxiety, nightmares, abnormal behaviour and psychoses have been alleged to persist long after the discontinuation of therapy. This example illustrates the need to balance all the risks of taking, or not taking, a prophylactic drug.

As with other anti-infective agents, there are also pharmacokinetic considerations. For example, care has to be taken in prescribing antimalarials to pregnant or lactating women. The overall risk to the unborn child from malaria is considered to be so much greater than the risk from the drugs, that the prevailing view is to give prophylactic treatment in pregnancy if exposure cannot be avoided (chloroquine and proguanil may be taken, but some other antimalarials are not advised). Folic acid supplements may be necessary if antimalarials that interfere with folate metabolism are taken. For most of the drugs, so little active component is excreted in breast milk that treatment can continue during breast feeding. Babies can also receive prophylactic treatment, and both chloroquine and proguanil can be prescribed from birth.

Another pharmacokinetic effect results from the time taken for the drug to rise to the blood concentrations needed to kill the parasites, and the need to maintain it close to this level throughout the risk period. For this reason, courses of chloroquine and proguanil are usually started at least two and a half weeks before likely exposure and continue for four weeks thereafter to 'mop up' parasites as they complete their life cycle. (The pre- and post-exposure periods are shorter for mefloquine.) It is important that daily or weekly dosage schedules should be taken at the same time each day or each week. The relationship between eating a meal and dosing also needs to be kept consistent to maintain appropriate blood levels of the active drug.

Such complex dosage regimens raise the issue of **compliance**, which is important for all anti-infective medication, and will be mentioned again in Section 2.10.1 in the context of the emergence of antimicrobial drug resistance. The term refers to the ability of the patient to *comply* with instructions given by health care providers about actions or behaviours expected to aid recovery or increase the effectiveness of treatment. Compliance is greatest when the patient participates in discussion about how therapy is to be delivered. In Section 6.5 of the *Tuberculosis* Case Study (which you should have studied by the end of this chapter), we discuss the more recent concept of *concordance*, which involves the patient fully in negotiating the treatment plan. Successful prophylaxis against malaria relies on self-dosing by the individuals concerned, and it is therefore highly desirable that the products in common use are active by oral administration

Summary of Section 2.8

1   Prophylactic chemotherapy is advised for individuals whose ability to resist infection is compromised by an underlying medical condition (e.g. cancer treatment, organ transplantation, cystic fibrosis), or when there is a known exposure to a high infection risk (e.g. during 'dirty' surgery, or contact with a potentially life-threatening pathogen as in mother-to-child HIV transmission).

2   The prophylactic use of antimalarial drugs prior to travel in an endemic area illustrates issues of drug selection on the basis of efficacy, parasite resistance, side effects, pharmacokinetics in certain patient groups (e.g. pregnant women), the maintenance of complex dosage regimens and compliance.

2.9 Alleviating the adverse consequences of infection

All the examples considered so far in this chapter have involved using chemotherapy (either prophylactically or post-exposure) to target the causative pathogen, or to reduce the risk of opportunistic pathogens gaining a hold. In this section, we consider therapeutic strategies aimed not at the pathogen, but at reducing the adverse consequences of the infectious disease it has caused. Such therapies may be used alongside anti-infective chemotherapy, or in some cases the body's own defence mechanisms may (by design or default) be left to fight the pathogens on their own. Drugs aimed at alleviating the consequences of an infection are usually prescribed for one or both the following reasons:

*   to provide symptom relief and support recovery;

*   to prevent damage to the infected individual's tissues, which in turn reduces the risk of subsequent health problems.

The range of prescription and over-the-counter medicines that can be used with these intentions is so large and varied that we will not attempt to review it here. Instead, we focus on readily available chemical remedies for alleviating the symptoms of two common categories of infectious disease: respiratory tract infections and acute diarrhoea.

2.9.1 Mitigating the symptoms of respiratory tract infections

Respiratory tract infections (RTIs) are generally categorized as either acute or chronic on the basis of their intensity and duration, as upper or lower RTIs depending on the location of the primary infection, and as viral or bacterial in origin.

○ Summarize the contribution of RTIs to the global burden of infectious disease.

● Acute respiratory infections cause more deaths worldwide than any other category of infectious disease; children under five years are worst affected (up to 2.2 million deaths annually, see Book 1, Figure 1.13). Even in advanced industrial economies, acute RTIs are the leading cause of death, mainly in old age, and relatively minor RTIs, such as the common cold, account for millions of episodes of illness and days lost from work and schooling. One of the most serious epidemic infections – influenza – is an acute RTI (Book 1, case study in Chapter 2). Chronic respiratory infections are a major cause of disability and death worldwide and include pulmonary tuberculosis (see the *Tuberculosis* Case Study associated with Book 2).

Self-administered treatments for viral 'flu-like illnesses and the common cold provide good examples of the principles involved in therapies aimed at symptom relief. The main symptoms of these conditions are fever, aches and pains, nasal congestion, sore throat and cough – varying in intensity from the minor inconvenience of a mild cold to the life-threatening respiratory collapse of a virulent influenza epidemic or SARS (severe acute respiratory syndrome). Most healthy adults are unlikely to suffer preventable primary damage from viral RTIs, but some do, and the young, especially babies, are much more vulnerable. The biggest danger in young children comes from *fever*, i.e. the elevation of body temperature above 37 °C.

○ Fever is a naturally-occurring response to many infections, mediated primarily by the cytokine interleukin-1 (Il-1; the mechanisms were described in Book 3, Section 2.3.5). How does raised body temperature contribute to host defences against pathogens?

● Lymphocyte proliferation is speeded up as body temperature rises, but pathogen replication is only marginally affected. It is advantageous to the host to produce as many lymphocytes with specific receptors for pathogen antigens as quickly as possible in the early phases of an infection, when it might be 'nipped in the bud'. Il-1 also suppresses appetite and increases sleepiness, so the fevered individual is more likely to rest and use all available energy to fuel immune defences rather than to digest food or for physical activity.

If body temperature rises no higher than about 40 °C in otherwise-healthy adults, the body functions adequately without sustaining harm. However, above this temperature, disruption of metabolic processes begins to occur that can ultimately prove fatal. High fevers can induce convulsions in young children because they do not have the same range of temperature-regulation mechanisms as older individuals. Fever is generally treated with physical methods of cooling the body and antipyretic (fever-reducing) medicines.

○ What antipyretic drug (or drugs) do common over-the-counter products to reduce fever contain?

● Usually they contain paracetamol, aspirin (recommended in the UK only for those aged 16 years or above), or ibuprofen (recommended in the UK only for those aged 12 years or above). These drugs may be formulated with other active ingredients that have other therapeutic actions.

Antipyretics alter the body's response to Il-1 and other fever-producing cytokines released during the infection, and bring about a drop in temperature. These drugs also tend to have analgesic (pain relieving) properties, so they alleviate aches, pains and sore throats. The effect most obvious to anxious parents of a fevered child is that the child becomes less distressed and usually drops into a peaceful sleep. This illustrates another benefit of addressing the adverse consequences of infection, namely that relief of symptoms can facilitate sleep and peaceful rest, and avoidance of complications associated with fatigue. The same is true of several other therapies for RTIs. Drugs that reduce nasal secretions or constrict blood vessels act by alleviating nasal and sinus congestion, which helps the sufferer to breathe more easily and sleep well and so recover more readily.

A serious consequence of RTIs, particularly in older people or smokers, is the development of bronchitis, a general term for inflammation of the airways, characterized by persistent coughing that typically produces quantities of phlegm, wheezing and difficulty in breathing. Secondary infections with bacteria proliferating in inflamed lung tissue are common, and chronic bronchitis can result in permanent damage to the airways and even the heart. Antibacterial drugs are generally prescribed to treat the infection directly, but a range of other drugs may also be needed to prevent or alleviate the adverse consequences for lung function. For example, groups with particular vulnerability to bronchial infections include people with lung disorders such as chronic obstructive pulmonary disease, asthma or emphysema. In these patients, oral or inhaled bronchodilator agents are often prescribed to reduce constriction in the airways, and anti-inflammatory agents can minimize the risk of permanent damage to lung tissue from chronic inflammation. As noted before, addressing the consequences of infection assists recovery. By enabling breathing to become easier, coughing is reduced, distress is lessened and a recovery is facilitated.

2.9.2 Treating diarrhoeal diseases

In the UK, episodes of diarrhoea are rarely life threatening even in the most vulnerable age groups, but elsewhere in the world, diarrhoea-inducing infections are a major cause of death, killing an estimated 1.7 million children aged under five every year (Book 1, Figure 1.12). Outbreaks of diarrhoeal diseases in developed countries are usually caused by virulent strains of indigenous food-borne bacteria (mainly salmonellae, campylobacter or *E.coli*), and some viruses (e.g. rotavirus). In developing countries, a much wider range of pathogens is responsible, including some with significant risk of mortality (e.g. *Shigella, Vibrio cholerae*). Despite differences in the infecting organisms, the therapeutic strategy for diarrhoeal diseases is the same wherever they occur. Although in some instances antimicrobials are prescribed to attack the causative pathogen, the essential intervention is to manage the damaging effects of acute diarrhoea on the host.

○ How can acute diarrhoea lead to death?

● As the *Cholera* Case Study (associated with Book 2) explained, infection of the gut wall causes leakage of key electrolytes (sodium, chloride, potassium and bicarbonate ions) from the tissues into the gut lumen. As the concentration of these ions rises in the gut contents, water is 'pulled' from the tissues into the gut lumen along the osmotic gradient (i.e. water molecules move so as to *equalize* the concentration of ions between the gut lumen and the surrounding tissues), resulting in rapid dehydration of body tissues as water is excreted in copious watery diarrhoea. Loss of potassium ions from the tissues causes muscle cramps and other neuromuscular problems. Loss of bicarbonate upsets the pH balance of the body, with consequent disruption of metabolic processes, which can be fatal. Blood pressure falls, cardiac output drops, muscle weakness is experienced, the amount of blood perfusing the major organs declines and death is usually due to kidney failure.

The universally recommended treatment for acute diarrhoea is **oral rehydration**, a low-cost and simple means to reverse the dehydration and restore the electrolyte balance. The life-saving potential of simple rehydrating agents cannot be overestimated and it is hard to imagine that any other therapy will ever have greater cost-effectiveness. Since the WHO began promoting oral rehydration therapy in 1979, the annual death toll among children from diarrhoeal diseases has fallen from around 5 million to under 2 million.

The WHO recommends that a solution of **oral rehydration salts (ORS)** should have the general composition shown in Table 2.4; the 'reduced osmolarity' formula was recommended for children from 2002 onwards (WHO/UNICEF, 2002). Many variations are in use or are being assessed, but whichever mix is used, the ingredients are dissolved in clean water (boiled and cooled for infants under 12 months). The dosage is proportional to the output of diarrhoea and the age of the person: for every loose motion, adults require 400 ml, children 100 ml and infants 50 ml of ORS, taken in small sips every 5 or 10 minutes. Pre-prepared sachets of the ORS mixture are widely available at low cost or are distributed free, but a home-made solution of one level teaspoon of table salt plus eight level teaspoons of sugar dissolved in a litre of clean drinking water is generally sufficient to save a life. Adults and older children should drink about three litres of ORS daily until symptoms remit.

TABLE 2.4 WHO recommended composition for solutions of oral rehydration salts (ORS).

Substance	Mass/g per litre of water	
	conventional formula	reduced osmolarity formula
sodium chloride	3.5	2.6
potassium chloride	1.5	1.5
trisodium citrate	2.9	2.9
glucose	20.0	13.5

To understand the principle of oral rehydration, consider the normal route of absorption of sodium ions (Na^+) across the epithelial layer of the gut lumen. The surface of the healthy gut lumen has numerous folds that provide a large surface area for absorption, and these are covered in a single layer of epithelial cells (Figure 2.11). Typically, 25 g of sodium (in ionic form) is secreted into the lumen of the gut each day as a constituent of the numerous gut secretions and a further 5 g typically enters the gut in food (together this accounts for about 15% of body sodium). Sodium ions are absorbed from the gut by an active (energy-using) process that is greatly facilitated by the presence of glucose in the gut lumen, which is also absorbed into the epithelial cells. As the sodium ion concentration rises in the epithelial cells, water is drawn into them from the gut lumen along the osmotic gradient. As sodium ions pass out of the epithelial layer and into the interstitial spaces before entering nearby blood vessels, the change in concentration draws water in the same direction, so blood volume rises. Normally, 95% of the water in the gut lumen is absorbed into the body by this process.

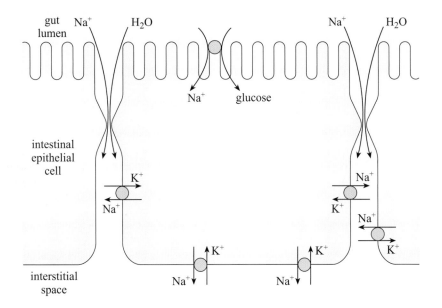

FIGURE 2.11
Diagram showing the major route by which water is absorbed across the intestinal epithelium. Simple sugars such as glucose are co-absorbed with sodium ions (Na^+) from the gut lumen into the epithelial cells, creating a concentration gradient which 'pulls' water molecules across the epithelium by osmosis. Na^+ can also flow in passively by this route. The sodium pump (pink circles) maintains the osmotic gradient by pumping Na^+ out of the epithelium into the interstitial spaces between cells, exchanging it for potassium ions (K^+).

○ Explain how drinking a solution with the composition in Table 2.4 alleviates the dehydration and other life-threatening effects of acute diarrhoea.

● The presence of sodium and glucose in the gut lumen at concentrations that optimally facilitate their absorption across the epithelium creates an osmotic gradient, which in turn increases the absorption of water from the gut into the blood stream. The electrolytes in the ORS help to restore the pH of body tissues and potassium-dependent neuromuscular functions, and glucose supplies an energy source in the period when no other nutrients can be absorbed.

There is unanimity about the value of ORS for the treatment of acute diarrhoea, but another method of symptom control remains controversial. Diarrhoea in adults can be treated with antimotility (gut motility reducing) agents, which reduce the muscular movements of the small intestine in particular. It has been argued that halting diarrhoea can be counterproductive because it is a defence mechanism by which the body rids itself of damaging organisms or toxins. However, current evidence shows that the use of antimotility agents does reduce the duration of diarrhoea without prolonging other symptoms. Synthetic opioid drugs tend to be the favoured agents at present, replacing morphine and opium used in the past, although in the UK several medicines based on a mixture of opiates and clays are still available (e.g. kaolin and morphine). However, the key to successful recovery is to maintain hydration and electrolyte balance until the pathogens are eliminated by the actions of the immune system.

Summary of Section 2.9

1   Chemicals can be used to prevent or treat the adverse consequences of infection. Over-the-counter remedies for respiratory tract infections include antipyretic drugs to reduce fever, analgesics to reduce pain and decongestants to reduce nasal secretions. Prescription drugs may include bronchodilators to reduce constriction of the airways (for example in bronchitis in people with lung disease) or anti-inflammatory agents.

2   The dehydration and electrolyte loss associated with acute diarrhoea can be reversed by drinking equivalent amounts of a solution of oral rehydration salts (ORS) prepared from simple ingredients (salt and sugar) or using low-cost sachets.

2.10 Access to chemical strategies

So far in this chapter, we have discussed the application of anti-infective chemicals without reference to factors that influence whether or not a product can actually be used in the treatment and control of an infectious disease. In this final section, we consider what stands in the way of providing effective medicines and biocides to tackle infectious diseases worldwide. Ignoring short-term problems with manufacture or supply, the main barriers to access are of four general types:

1   *Inadequate scientific knowledge.* There are large gaps in the chemical 'arsenal' where no effective product exists. Science may have tried and repeatedly failed to develop an effective drug against a particular pathogen, or research may simply not have been pursued.

2   *Drug resistance.* Chemicals that were once effective may have become useless because their target pathogens have evolved mechanisms that enable them to survive chemical attack.

3   *Cost.* Effective medicines may exist, but are beyond the financial reach of individuals who must pay for them, or local or national health services that cannot afford to purchase them.

4   *Political or cultural factors.* Official policies and/or the views of opinion leaders and influential groups may prevent, discourage or restrict access to effective medicines.

○   What major infectious diseases cannot yet be successfully treated or controlled by chemical interventions because basic scientific knowledge is lacking?

●   Even though the symptoms of some major viral diseases (e.g. influenza, herpes infections) can be alleviated by medication, and the progression of HIV to AIDS can be slowed by antiretroviral drugs, there are still no effective chemical 'cures' for any viral infection within the body. Despite decades of research, there are as yet no safe and effective drugs to eliminate the parasites causing malaria or sleeping sickness; (Chapter 4 includes a case study on guinea worm – another parasite that cannot be treated chemically). Although there are chemical controls for many bacterial and fungal infections, some pathogens can damage the host's tissues or disrupt metabolism so rapidly that they often prove fatal or cause irreversible disability (as in meningococcal or tubercular meningitis). Vector control has also had limited success.

Scientific knowledge is also continuously being overtaken by the evolution of drug resistance in pathogenic strains and vector species. We consider this problem next, before turning to the other barriers to accessibility of anti-infective agents.

2.10.1 Microbial and parasite resistance

The development of resistance to anti-infective chemicals by microbial pathogens, parasites and their vectors or secondary hosts is an increasingly serious threat to health in the modern world. The number of drug-resistant organisms is rising, as is the number of people suffering the consequences of the illness and disability they cause, and the cost of overcoming the resistance is spiralling upwards (e.g. drug-resistant TB costs US$2000–8000 per person to treat, compared with about $20 for drugs against susceptible strains; WHO, 2000). Although it is legitimate to claim that drug resistance has, in part, resulted from inappropriate use of chemical agents, it must be recognized that the development of resistance to chemical or other environmental selection pressures is an inevitable consequence of adaptive evolution. The use of chemical agents exerts selection pressure on pathogen and parasite populations, driving them towards greater resistance because the best adapted are most likely to survive to reproduce a new generation of offspring, each with their parent's adaptive advantage (recall Book 1, Box 1.4).

○   What biological mechanism increases the speed of transmission of 'resistance genes' in bacterial populations?

●   Plasmids are particularly important in spreading drug-resistance genes (Book 2, Box 2.2) because they can be transmitted 'horizontally' within and between bacterial species, and different plasmids can also recombine within a cell to generate new combinations of resistance genes.

However, if evolutionary processes dictate that we cannot avoid the development of some degree of microbial or parasite resistance to chemical agents, we can still find ways to reduce the transmission of resistant organisms from person to person, to prevent the development of multi-drug resistance and to ameliorate the damage that resistant strains cause. There are three strands to this containment strategy:

*   the development and production of new anti-infective agents against hitherto resistant targets, or with greater efficacy or a broader spectrum of activity;

*   the agreement and implementation of policies and procedures to reduce the development of resistance to existing chemical agents;

*   the monitoring of compliance with these policies and procedures by patients, health care workers and prescribers.

The development of new anti-infective chemicals will be discussed in Section 2.10.2, but the other two strands are interrelated and will be discussed together here.

Research studies have repeatedly shown that in any community (e.g. a hospital, a region, a country), the better the control exercised over the use of anti-infective chemicals, the less damage is caused by drug-resistant organisms. Despite this, policies vary enormously within and between nations, partly because of economic factors and partly because of historic custom. Even when the European Union's Council of Ministers agreed (in 2001) on formal guidelines for the prudent use of antibiotics and other antimicrobial agents, the recommendations were non-binding on member states. The essential elements of the strategy to control drug-resistant organisms in the UK are listed in Box 2.8 overleaf.

> ### BOX 2.8   Strategies to control drug-resistant organisms
>
> 1   Restrict the range of anti-infective chemicals in use to those most appropriate for the task.
>
> 2   Keep some powerful anti-infective chemicals in reserve as 'last ditch' treatments.
>
> 3   Ensure that every use of an anti-infective results in destruction of as close to 100% of the target organisms as possible.
>
> 4   Ensure that transmission of resistant organisms from one human host to another is reduced as much as possible.
>
> 5   Control and monitor the use of anti-infectives in food production and veterinary practice.

All five of the UK strategies outlined in Box 2.8 apply both to anti-infective medicines administered to patients and to biocides used as disinfectants, sterilizing fluids, etc. Strategies 1 and 2 are based on the common sense premise that the fewer anti-infectives in use, the fewer will induce resistance in target organisms. Avoidance of unnecessary prescribing is an important element in this strategy, in that the fewer organisms that ever make contact with the chemical, the fewer instances of resistance there are likely to be. If, for example, a hospital restricts itself to using a small range of antibacterials for a defined period, and then switches to another range thereafter, it may be able to avoid becoming a reservoir of bacteria with resistance to both groups of drugs. If any resistance to the first group of chemicals starts to emerge, then switching products increases the likelihood that the bacteria will be destroyed by the second group and the resistance will be eliminated.

It may seem obvious that when anti-infective chemicals are chosen for use, they must be those whose activity is known to be appropriate for the infectious agents concerned. However, the initial diagnosis of most common infections – even in advanced industrial nations – does not usually involve identification of the infective organism. One element in the anti-resistance strategy is therefore to increase the level of testing of pathogens for drug-susceptibility before making prescribing decisions. In addition, if the most potent chemical is held back from use in all except the most life-threatening circumstances, it may be possible to avoid resistance developing to the product of 'last resort'.

☐   In response to claims in the UK that antibacterial drugs were being over-prescribed, there has been a fall in recent years in prescriptions of antibacterials for patients with chest infections. What are the potential costs and benefits of this trend for patients?

●   There is a possibility that some patients in need of antibacterial therapy will not receive it (the recorded rise in incidence of pneumonia may be a consequence of changes in the prescribing culture (Price *et al.*, 2002)). Conversely, if restricting the use of antibacterials reduces the rise in drug-resistant bacteria, then patients will be less likely to suffer from persistent or untreatable infections.

The problem of over-prescription or inappropriate use of antibacterial drugs is not restricted to the health systems of advanced industrial economies like the UK. An estimated 50–70% of antibacterial usage in the developing world may be inappropriately applied (WHO, 2000). The widespread sale of antibacterial drugs 'over the counter', including injectable antibiotics, by unlicensed pharmacies or street traders is increasingly being linked to the emergence of multi-drug resistant strains of bacteria in many parts of Africa and Asia. The reasons for concern are illustrated by a study of drug sales in Cameroon, where the researchers reported that antibacterials:

> … are commonly provided for non-specific symptoms (such as headache, fatigue, nausea, myalgias or fever) without medical assessment or diagnostic testing. Even when indicated, inadequate dosing or an incomplete course of antibiotic treatment is the norm.

> (Becker *et al.,* 2002, p. 325)

This type of usage breaches the third strategy in Box 2.8 – the requirement that anti-infectives destroy as close to 100% of the target organisms as possible. As discussed earlier in this chapter, chemicals with a high degree of efficacy should be used, taking into account all pharmacokinetic considerations in designing the correct dosage regimen, delivered by the optimum route and for a sufficient duration to eliminate the infection. Failure to prescribe correctly, or to comply with the recommendations for optimal usage, encourages the development of drug-resistant strains, which can be passed on to new hosts and may re-establish a resistant infection in the original patient.

The need to reduce transmission of pathogens from person-to-person (strategy 4 in Box 2.8) may seem obvious, particularly in health care institutions (as the case study on hospital acquired infections, Book 1, Chapter 4, illustrated), but it is an aspect that is often neglected. For example, in busy hospital wards with overstretched health care staff, simple rules such as effective hand-washing between attending to two patients can be rushed, ignored or forgotten. All surfaces of the hands must be in contact with the correct strength of antiseptic agent for an appropriate period, or the required standard of hand antisepsis will not be met (testing of hand-washing agents was discussed in Section 2.3.2, see Table 2.2). According to a press report in 2002, the Director of the UK Laboratory of Hospital Infection at the Central Public Health Laboratory admitted to:

> … lying awake at night trying to think of ways to persuade health care workers that washing their hands saves lives.

> (Neill, 2002)

However, some attempts to reduce bacterial contamination may be counter-productive. Increasingly, consumers in wealthier countries are being encouraged to use biocides (e.g. disinfectant kitchen wipes and sprays) for domestic tasks previously undertaken with non-biocidal cleaning products. In the mid-1990s, there were relatively few antibacterial household products on the market, but a review of their availability in the USA in 2001 identified more than 700, including utensils, storage containers and bed linen impregnated with biocides (Levy, 2001).

○ What long-term disadvantages could arise from this trend?

● Biocidal sprays and wipes are not always used optimally; household goods impregnated with biocides exert a continuous low-level selection pressure on microbial populations. This usage contradicts strategies 1–3 in Box 2.8 and there is growing concern that it will promote the development of resistant microbes in domestic environments.

During the latter half of the twentieth century, antibacterial drugs were also increasingly used in animal husbandry to prevent infection and boost the growth of livestock (strategy 5 in Box 2.8), consuming about 50% of global production (WHO, 2000). While it is undoubtedly the case that drug-resistant bacteria have been identified in farmed animals and that resistance can be transferred from animals to people, there is controversy about the risk this poses to human health (for a review, see Singer *et al.,* 2003). However, there is widespread agreement that the control, monitoring and careful selection of anti-infectives for veterinary or agricultural use are just as necessary as they are in human health care.

2.10.2 Development of new products

Although strategies other than the use of chemicals are successfully employed to combat infection (as Chapters 3 to 5 illustrate), it is apparent that, for the foreseeable future, there will be a continued need for new anti-infective chemical products. Here we will focus on the development of new medicines, but you should note that similar needs, issues and problems arise in the context of new vector control chemicals (e.g. insecticides and molluscicides), and new biocidal chemicals for disinfection, sterilization and antisepsis. New medicines are required where:

* no adequate treatment for infected patients currently exists;

* organisms have developed resistance to existing treatments;

* existing treatments are poorly tolerated;

* existing treatments are too expensive, or at least not cost-effective.

It is worth noting that the last point in the list above can apply to relatively prosperous countries, as well as to developing nations with low incomes. In the UK for example, the Department of Health sets cost-efficacy standards for the prescription of drugs to treat certain conditions, taking into account the cost of the drug and the benefit to the patient in terms of quantity and quality of life. Drugs that offer relatively low 'health gain' at high cost are not generally available as NHS prescriptions. But even when an expensive drug is shown to be cost-effective for *individuals*, fundholders may not authorize its use for their *populations* because the potential drain on limited resources is considered to be too great. An example of an anti-infective drug with this status is zanamivir, which alleviates flu-like illnesses but is not generally prescribed for moderate symptoms; however, it would be an important defence in an influenza epidemic.

There is no certainty that pharmaceutical research will be able to develop anti-infective agents to 'close the gaps' in provision, as the challenge presented by HIV clearly illustrates. At the start of the twenty-first century, the main anti-infective research effort is focused on developing new antibacterial drugs that can attack resistant bacteria (particularly the multi-drug resistant *Mycobacterium tuberculosis* strains, and the bacterial agents of meningitis), antiviral agents (particularly directed against HIV, hepatitis B and C viruses and human papilloma virus), and antimalarial drugs capable of killing resistant *Plasmodium* species. Pharmaceutical companies have been accused of neglecting research into some other infectious diseases, particularly sleeping sickness, Chagas' disease, leishmaniasis and trachoma (for example, see Yamey and Torreele, 2002).

Critics claim that some diseases are under-researched because they offer too low a financial return on the investment required to bring a new drug to market. However,

2 CHEMICAL STRATEGIES AGAINST INFECTION

the sums involved are very large – estimated at between US$240 million and $802 million per product. Sometimes the reasons for not searching for a chemical solution are because a better alternative exists. For example, there are no effective drugs to treat polio, but the worldwide availability of an effective vaccine means that there is no incentive for drug companies to commit the huge sums required to develop anti-polio medicines. (A case study on polio is associated with Chapter 3 of this book.)

The accelerating pace of the research effort can be gauged by the doubling of research expenditure by the pharmaceutical industry in the 1990s, to reach US$45 billion in 2002, but this is set against the global sales of drugs being worth over $400 billion annually (Taylor, 2003). The scale and complexity of the effort needed to produce a new therapeutic agent is not always recognized. Taking the whole range of therapeutic medicines, fewer than 30 new chemical entities reach the worldwide market in some years and the numbers are steadily falling. We do not have the space here to explore the complex reasons for the declining output of new drugs, but economic considerations are at the forefront. The hope is that rapidly advancing scientific knowledge of pathogen genomes will enable a new generation of 'smart drugs' to be designed. It is no accident that *Plasmodium* and its *Anopheles* vector are among the first non-human species to be genome sequenced.

Trials of new chemical entities

The new drugs licensed for use every year are the rare successes among hundreds of thousands of chemical entities examined, virtually all of which are rejected during the development process. Typically, a period of at least seven or eight years will elapse between the identification of a potentially useful molecule and its first commercial launch. The process starts with the design or discovery of a new chemical entity. Invertebrates such as moths and worms, and vertebrates such as sharks, frogs and alligators, are increasingly being investigated as sources of naturally-occurring antimicrobials. If the chemical shows promise in initial laboratory tests, it will be patented and subjected to systematic testing of safety and efficacy. Safety assessments include acute tolerability (short-term high-dose application), toxicity tests for tissue damage, mutagenicity and carcinogenicity, allergenicity and teratogenicity (damage to foetal tissues). If laboratory tests of safety and efficacy yield promising data, the chemical will begin the first of three phases of **clinical trials** in humans.

Phase 1 trials assess dosage and tolerability in a small number of healthy volunteers. Phase 2 trials test the new chemical for efficacy and tolerability in well-defined groups of patients (e.g. children, pregnant women), so that pharmacokinetic effects can also be evaluated. Phase 2 trials often do not occur until 3–5 years after the development programme started and generally involve at most a few hundred patients. Phase 3 trials involve much larger groups of patients (usually thousands) and may have a 'multi-centre' design, with different research teams evaluating the outcomes in different locations. During the Phase 3 trials, attempts will be made to get the formulated chemical registered in the countries in which it is to be launched. In many countries, the product can only be used after approval by a national agency, and even then there will be issues to settle over who will pay for it (the patient, an insurer, a health care scheme) and at what price. (For an insight into the process from initial identification to registration of a new antimalarial drug, see Lang and Greenwood (2003) under *Course Resources* on the course website.)

Patenting new products

From the brief description above, it is not hard to see that there is abundant scope for efficacy, safety, commercial and political disputes to arise in the development of a new chemical entity. All of these disputes have the capacity to delay the therapeutic application of a scientific discovery, but the issue that has attracted most attention in recent years has been patent protection and its ability to influence the availability of newer and potent products in poorer countries. The security of their patents is a major concern to the pharmaceutical companies, who argue that strong patent protection is essential for their survival as innovators.

There is no better example of a failure to supply key medicines than that in the late 1990s involving delays in the provision of anti-HIV medicines to the population of South Africa – the country with the highest HIV population prevalence in the world.

○ From your reading of reports in the media around the turn of the millennium, what factors contributed to this delay?

◉ They included the initial high price of branded anti-HIV medicines, which would have cost more than the entire national health budget; legal action by drug companies to protect their patent rights by challenging South Africa's decision to import cheaper generic (non-branded) anti-HIV medicines from pharmaceutical factories in India and Thailand; doubts expressed by key members of the South African government (including President Mbeke) about the link between HIV and AIDS and the need for drug treatments; and concerns about whether the essential infrastructure was in place to ensure adequate drug distribution and compliance with such a complex drug regimen.

Only in 2002 were agreements reached with the drug companies that allowed affordable access to anti-HIV medicines in South Africa, primarily to reduce mother-to-child transmission.

The issues surrounding the supply of these drugs are discussed elsewhere (*Reference* CD-ROM, U205, Book 8, Chapter 4), but note that they do not eliminate the virus from the body, and sub-optimal drug regimens promote the evolution of drug-resistant strains. Although this dispute did not influence research and development of new anti-HIV products, because there was demand and supply in other countries, it is not hard to see how such disputes have the potential to reduce the effort and investment put into searching for therapies for diseases that are mostly found in poorer countries. Regrettably, many of the issues at stake are only likely to be resolved within wider international trade agreements and at a slow pace. Meanwhile, there is an urgent need for collaboration between patent holders, manufacturers, distributors, research fund-holders, health care providers and politicians to find ways of overcoming the drug-availability barriers in the developing world.

Fortunately there are positive developments, including a growing trend for groups of interested parties to enter into collaborations and partnerships focused on objectives specified in the WHO Essential Drugs Programme (a programme fostering universal access to a list of essential medicines in developing countries). The UN Accelerating Access Initiative (AAI) has achieved some modest success. The World Trade Organisation has issued a declaration on the TRIPS Agreement (which governs trade-related intellectual property rights), stating that member states can grant licenses to produce their own generic drugs in 'a national emergency', identifying HIV/AIDS, malaria and TB as public-health crises. International travel and business provide further drivers for the development of new medicines and vaccines to protect business travellers and tourists, or to deal with imported cases of non-endemic diseases.

Summary of Section 2.10

1   Access to anti-infective chemicals is influenced by gaps in scientific knowledge, the huge cost of developing new products, and political, economic and logistical constraints in both the developed and developing world.

2   Drug resistance increasingly threatens access to medical treatment. Strategies to limit it include controlling the medical, domestic and agricultural use of anti-infective agents, ensuring that usage is maximally effective, and preventing transmission of resistant strains.

3   Major gaps in the chemical arsenal are the lack of any 'curative' antiviral drugs, poor efficacy or availability of drugs to treat several major parasitic diseases, and new products to replace those rendered obsolete by multi-drug resistant strains.

4   Development of new chemical entities takes several years from identification of an active molecule, through laboratory tests of safety and efficacy and three phases of human clinical trials, to the marketing of a new product. Pharmaceutical companies argue that patent protection is essential for innovation, due to the high cost of developing the small number of new products licensed for use each year.

Learning outcomes for Chapter 2

When you have studied this chapter you should be able to:

2.1   Define and use, or recognize definitions and applications of, each of the terms printed in **bold** in the text. *(Question 2.1)*

2.2   Discuss a range of factors that influence the efficacy, selectivity and pharmacokinetics of anti-infective chemicals and explain why they must be considered when setting guidelines on conditions of use. *(Questions 2.2, 2.3 and 2.4)*

2.3   Describe a variety of physico-chemical and biochemical properties of anti-infective agents that can be utilized for infection control inside and outside the body, and comment on ways in which chemical activity may be disrupted. *(Questions 2.4, 2.5 and 2.6)*

2.4   Illustrate the circumstances in which anti-infective chemicals may be used prophylactically. *(Questions 2.5 and 2.6)*

2.5   Give examples of chemical interventions that operate prior to or following significant exposure to infectious agents, to reduce microbial or parasite contamination, tackle vectors in the environment, prevent or arrest an infection, or alleviate its adverse consequences on the host. *(Question 2.6)*

2.6   Discuss the rationales for using anti-infective chemicals singly, or in combinations (multiple therapy), and illustrate the potential advantages and problems of each approach. *(Question 2.7)*

2.7 Demonstrate an awareness of the scientific, economic and political challenges and problems associated with current usage of chemicals to control and manage infectious diseases. *(Questions 2.6 and 2.7)*

Questions for Chapter 2

Question 2.1

Alcohols have been described as having a rapid 'bactericidal activity' and being 'sporistatic'. What do you understand these terms to mean?

Question 2.2

In the nineteenth century, Paul Ehrlich thought that an acceptable level of selective toxicity could be achieved if the maximum tolerated dose of a drug was about five times the minimal curative dose. Why is this ratio now considered too simplistic for modern guidelines on selective toxicity?

Question 2.3

Is their smaller body size the only reason for prescribing lower doses of anti-infective medicines to young children than to adults?

Question 2.4

Many bacteria use unique intracellular enzymes to undertake key metabolic reactions, which are essential for their survival and replication. These enzymes are potential targets for antibacterial chemicals. Suppose a chemical was shown to inhibit a sample of a bacterial enzyme in laboratory tests, but failed to show activity against the bacteria infecting a human host. What explanations would you suggest?

Question 2.5

Give two examples of chemical analogues of naturally-occurring molecules that have been used as anti-infective drugs, and explain their mode of action. Under what circumstances might each of these drugs (in theory) have some prophylactic value?

Question 2.6

Summarize the chemical strategies described in this chapter aimed at preventing the transmission of malarial parasites by mosquitoes. What are the main problems with these approaches?

Question 2.7

Taking a broad view of the issues, what are the main problems associated with the use of antiretroviral drugs in the treatment of people with HIV infection?

3 VACCINATION

The chapter begins with the early history of smallpox – the first infectious disease to be eradicated by a vaccination programme. The structure of the vaccinia virus (used in the vaccine), the replication cycle of the smallpox virus and the pathology it causes were discussed in Book 2; it would be useful to revise Figures 3.8 and 3.15 briefly and the effects of smallpox on the host (p.82) before commencing this chapter. At the end of Section 3.1, we ask you to read an article on the history of smallpox (accessed online via a link from the S320 home page). Then, before continuing further with Chapter 3, you should turn to the *Polio* Case Study, where we discuss the prospects for making this the second infectious disease to be eradicated by vaccination. At the end of Section 3.5 you will study the 'Vaccination' mini-lecture on *Immunology Interactive* CD2. You will conclude your study of this chapter by conducting some Internet research on the progress of vaccination programmes.

3.1 Smallpox and the history of vaccination

Undoubtedly, one of the great success stories of modern medicine has been in the field of vaccination against infectious diseases. There is no more compelling example than smallpox. It is hard now to imagine the impact of smallpox, which killed 10–50% (sometimes more) of the people it infected and wiped out whole communities. In the nineteenth century, the English parliamentary historian Thomas Macaulay graphically described its effects:

> Smallpox was always present, filling the churchyard with corpses, tormenting with constant fear all whom it had not yet stricken, leaving on those whose lives it spared the hideous traces of its power, turning the babe into a changeling at which the mother shuddered, and making the eyes and cheeks of the betrothed maiden objects of horror to the lover.

> (From *The History of England from the Accession of James II* by Thomas Macaulay, completed 1855)

Smallpox, caused by the variola virus, is thought to have originated in the first agricultural settlements in North Africa and was one of the greatest scourges of humanity for at least 10 000 years. It holds a special place in the history of immunology and infectious disease as the first disease for which an effective vaccine was developed and the first to be eradicated globally (confirmed by the WHO in 1980).

3.1.1 Variolation

By the seventeenth century, the observation that immunity from severe smallpox followed a mild episode of the disease had led to the practice of 'variolation' in China and the Ottoman Empire. **Variolation** was so named because material was taken from dried scabs or pustules (the Latin *varus*, 'marks on the skin') and used deliberately to infect healthy recipients. Infected material could be applied to an area of scarified skin or could be introduced into the nose as a dust. The material was taken from people with a milder form of the disease (possibly caused by variola minor virus). Although there was no understanding of either the immune system or infectious agents at that time, the effect was to expose the recipient to a supposedly 'weaker' strain of the virus, which elicited a protective immune response against subsequent infection with a more virulent strain.

○ What key features of the immune response does the practice of variolation demonstrate? (If you are unsure, revise Book 3, Section 2.11.)

● It shows the *specificity* of the immune response (variolation with smallpox material protected recipients specifically against this disease) and the existence of *immunological memory* (it resulted in long-lasting protection).

Variolation was usually followed by a fever and the treated area of skin developed an acute inflammatory response with the characteristic 'pox' lesions. Although recovery usually ensued, 2–3% of people could be killed by the smallpox infection that resulted from the procedure.

○ Why would a 'medical' procedure with a 2–3% fatality rate be tolerated?

● The risk of fatality from variolation was still much less than that of contracting a fatal smallpox infection.

FIGURE 3.1
Portrait of Edward Jenner painted in about 1800 by William Pearce. Note the cows in the background, the source of the cowpox virus he used to vaccinate people against smallpox.

Variolation was introduced into Europe early in the eighteenth century (you will learn more about this period when you read the article at the end of this section), where it gradually became known as *inoculation* (from the Latin for 'to graft or implant').

3.1.2 Edward Jenner and vaccination with cowpox

Vaccination originally meant deliberate infection with the cowpox virus (vaccinia), which is responsible for a relatively benign infection on the udders of cows and can be transferred to people, where it usually causes pustules on the hands. However, serious complications can ensue in a minority of cases. Vaccination with cowpox developed from an experiment carried out by an English country doctor, Edward Jenner (Figure 3.1). He had heard the common folklore that milkmaids who became infected with cowpox appeared to be protected from smallpox, and it had been previously reported that people who had recovered from cowpox did not develop the usual skin reaction to variolation. In 1796, Jenner deliberately infected an eight-year-old boy with the cowpox virus and repeated the experiment on ten others in the next two years. He confirmed that these vaccinated subjects did not respond to smallpox variolation and, despite initial resistance (Figure 3.2), his work ushered in the era of protective immunisation. In

FIGURE 3.2 A cartoon by James Gillray, published in 1801, depicting Edward Jenner at the Smallpox Inoculation Hospital, St Pancras, London, vaccinating the populace with cowpox, which (according to the original caption) had 'wonderful effects!'

honour of Jenner, the term **vaccination** became widely used for any procedure in which the aim is to produce or enhance immunity to an infectious agent. In this chapter, we follow this tradition, but note that vaccination and immunisation are equivalent terms in current usage.

☐ The type of vaccination developed by Jenner used one kind of pox virus to produce immunity against another. How can an immune response against one antigen or pathogen be effective against another? Does this not go against the idea that immune responses are 'specific'?

◼ Recall the idea of cross-reactivity (Book 3, Section 2.1.4). An antibody that binds to an epitope (a particular molecular shape) on one antigen will also bind to another antigen if it shares an identical epitope, or a very similar one. Two viruses may have sufficiently similar epitopes that an antibody raised against one will also bind to the other. Antibody specificity is not absolute.

Although it was the first to be discovered, this type of vaccination – using one pathogen to protect against another with which it cross-reacts – is quite unusual. Much more common is the use of killed pathogens, or a harmless variant of the pathogen, or one of its component antigens, to induce immunity without producing disease. We look at modern methods of vaccine production in Section 3.4.

3.1.3 Is smallpox still a threat?

Since the smallpox virus was declared eradicated 'in the wild' in 1980, stocks of virus have been held in secure laboratories in various parts of the world, with the expectation that they would eventually be destroyed. However, since 2001, the perceived threat of bioterrorism has led to debates about whether they should be retained as a vital resource for research into ways to combat a deliberate release of smallpox virus – assuming that samples have been (or could be) obtained by terrorist groups. Mathematical models of how smallpox might spread through a population have been constructed (using the principles discussed in Book 6), and the effects of vaccinating people with vaccinia either before or after a theoretical exposure have also been modelled. (If you are interested in following up the details, there are some links on the course website, under *Course Resources*).

Vaccination programmes ended over 20 years ago, so even those individuals who were vaccinated as children are unlikely now to be protected against smallpox (i.e. almost everyone is susceptible), but a decision on whether to reintroduce smallpox vaccination is not straightforward. Serious complications of injecting people with vaccinia can be expected to occur in a minority of individuals – particularly those with immunodeficiency. In the 1960s, smallpox vaccination led to an estimated 1–3 deaths per million doses, but today's population now has very much larger numbers of people whose immune system is suppressed by HIV infection or medical treatment (e.g. for cancer), or following organ transplants. The vaccine contains 'live' vaccinia, so even if its recipients are selected to be in good health, they can pass the virus on to others who may be less able to withstand its pathological effects.

So the question of whether the risks of reintroducing smallpox vaccination outweigh the possible benefits depends on estimates of the potential risk of a bioterrorist attack. At the time of writing (2003) the threat is considered to be so low that vaccination has only been reintroduced in the UK and USA for health workers who would be in the 'front line' of any response to an outbreak.

Summary of Section 3.1

1   Smallpox, caused by the variola virus, was one of the great pandemic infectious diseases for more than 10 000 years, killing a high proportion of infected people and changing the course of history.

2   Variolation in the seventeenth and eighteenth centuries used material from 'mild' smallpox cases to infect healthy people, most of whom developed protective immunity, but there was a 2–3% death rate.

3   In 1796 Edward Jenner began experiments that led to widespread vaccination with cowpox virus (vaccinia), which elicits antibodies that cross-react with variola and protect against smallpox. By 1980, vaccination had eradicated smallpox globally.

4   Since 2001, the costs and benefits of reintroducing smallpox vaccination have been debated in response to the possible threat of bioterrorism.

To find out more about the history of smallpox, you should now read an article by Barquet and Domingo entitled 'Smallpox: The Triumph over the Most Terrible of the Ministers of Death' (the title paraphrases another quotation from Thomas Macaulay). You can locate it online by following the links to Book 7 topics under *Course Resources* on the S320 website. We suggest that you don't read the final section of the article (on deadlines for destroying all remaining stocks of smallpox virus), which has been overtaken by subsequent events. After you have read the essay, answer Question 3.2 at the end of the chapter.

Then read the *Polio* Case Study, where we discuss the biology and epidemiology of polio and reflect on the global vaccination programme, which aims to eradicate it from the world by 2005. You should allow around three hours for this, including some time for exploration of WHO and UNICEF websites, which publish regularly updated information on the progress of the polio eradication campaign. There is also an optional visit to a website on the social history of polio epidemics in the USA in the twentieth century.

TABLE 3.1
Year of first use anywhere of a vaccine against some major infectious diseases.

Infectious disease	First use
smallpox	1798
rabies	1885
cholera	1885
tetanus antitoxin (passive)	1890
diphtheria antitoxin (passive)	1893
anthrax	1891
typhoid	1896
plague	1897
diphtheria	1923
tuberculosis (BCG)	1923
tetanus	1924
pertussis (whooping cough)	1926
tetanus	1927
yellow fever	1935
hepatitis A (passive)	1945
polio (IPV)	1955
polio (OPV)	1962
measles	1963
mumps	1967
meningitis A	1969
rubella	1970
haemophilus influenza	1972
viral influenza	1976
meningitis C (polysaccharide)	1977
hepatitis B	1981
hepatitis A	1989
varicella zoster (chickenpox)	1995
meningitis C (conjugate)	1999

3.2 Active vaccines and passive immunisation

Since Jenner's pioneering discovery, many new vaccines have been developed (Table 3.1). The country in which a vaccine was first introduced is usually the one that developed it; France and the USA are among the most prominent: for example, rabies, plague and BCG vaccines were first used in France, polio vaccines were introduced first in the USA. There has often been a considerable time lag between dates of first use in the country in which a vaccine was pioneered and its adoption elsewhere (e.g. BCG vaccination was delayed in the UK until 1954), and some countries have never adopted particular vaccines. Some were immediately introduced in mass vaccination programmes (e.g. against polio), and others have only been used selectively to control outbreaks. Continuing research means that the 'first' vaccines against a particular infectious disease are superseded by more effective preparations. Some vaccines are now so effective that the infections they protect against are termed *vaccine-preventable diseases* – the WHO has placed the highest priority on achieving mass vaccination against diphtheria, whooping cough (pertussis), tetanus, measles, mumps, rubella, polio and TB.

The incidence of most of the diseases in Table 3.1 was declining in most countries in the world for some time before the introduction of the relevant vaccine, due to improvements in public health and living standards (as outlined in Chapter 1). However, the annual toll of mortality and morbidity was significantly greater than it is today and sharp declines in the incidence occurred when an effective vaccination programme was introduced, as Figure 3.3 overleaf and the *Polio* Case Study illustrate.

When people use the term vaccination, they nearly always mean **active vaccination**, i.e. immunising an individual with pathogen-specific antigens in order to induce a protective immune response against subsequent infection with that pathogen. The antigens in the vaccine elicit a *primary immune response*, which takes 7–14 days to reach its peak before subsiding. 'Booster' doses of the vaccine increase the protection against that infection by ensuring that it will be met by an enhanced *secondary immune response.*

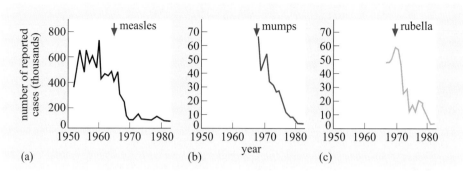

FIGURE 3.3 The annual incidence (number of reported cases × 1000) of three viral diseases in the USA, 1950–1980, showing the year (arrowed) in which vaccination programmes began. (Note the difference in scale on the vertical axis of the measles graph, which peaked at close to 800 000 cases in 1960, compared with the incidence of mumps and rubella.)

○ Explain why the antibodies produced during the secondary response are more effective than those of the primary response; (if you are unsure, revise Book 3, Section 2.1.5).

● There is a shorter lag time before pathogen-specific antibodies appear (typically 2–3 days); the overall level of antibodies is higher and they persist for longer; less IgM and more IgG is produced (due to class switching, Book 3, Section 2.10.5), which increases the protection in the blood stream; the affinity of the antibody binding sites for the target antigen is generally higher, so they bind more strongly.

In a small number of infectious diseases, active vaccines can also be given *therapeutically* to people who are already infected, to stimulate their immune system to eliminate the pathogens, or at least slow the progression of the disease. This approach is being tested extensively in trials of therapeutic vaccines against established HIV infection.

However, there is another type of procedure, termed **passive immunisation**, which is used therapeutically to treat particular infectious diseases after symptoms have developed, or for *post-exposure prophylaxis* (a term already discussed in Chapter 2 in relation to drug treatment). In passive immunisation, the recipient is directly injected with antibodies from another immune individual, who had either developed immunity following an infection or after immunisation with an active vaccine. The procedure is described as 'passive' because recipients do not manufacture the antibodies for themselves. Indeed, the presence of passively acquired antibodies may reduce the ability of recipients to manufacture their own antibodies (because of negative feedback controls operating in the immune system).

○ Under what circumstances would it be advantageous to give someone pre-prepared antibodies against an infectious agent?

● Passive immunisation is particularly important in certain life-threatening infections where there are no anti-infective drugs or they act too slowly; active vaccination takes too long to stimulate a protective immune response.

The most important infections in which passive immunisation is used are listed in Table 3.2. The use of passive immunisation often preceded the introduction of an active vaccine against certain infections (see Table 3.1 earlier).

Table 3.2 Current examples of passive immunisation.

Disease	Source of antibodies	Usage
tetanus	human or horse serum	after symptoms develop
diphtheria	human or horse serum	after symptoms develop
gangrene	horse serum	after exposure
botulism	horse serum	after exposure
hepatitis B	human serum	after exposure
rabies	human serum	after exposure (plus active vaccine)

○ Explain why pathogen-specific antibodies are given immediately to people with suspected tetanus, diphtheria or botulism. How do they protect the patient?

● All three bacterial diseases are caused by a potentially fatal exotoxin (Book 2, Section 2.4.1), and it is imperative to neutralize it in the blood as quickly as possible. The passively acquired antibodies bind to the toxin, which can no longer bind to host cells or disrupt metabolic processes. The toxin-antibody complexes are usually destroyed by phagocytosis.

Passive immunisation is also used for some serious viral diseases such as rabies, where the antiserum is administered after exposure to the infected bite, together with active vaccination (see Table 3.2). Passively administered antibodies can also be important for individuals who suffer from certain immunodeficiencies in which they cannot manufacture their own antibodies. Such people are extremely susceptible to many types of infection and administration of pooled human antibodies (which contain a mixture of protective antibodies against many pathogens) can keep them in health. As Table 3.2 shows, some antisera for passive immunisation may be raised in horses by injecting them with the antigen and later using their serum as a source of specific antibodies.

○ What problems would you expect to result from infusing human subjects repeatedly with horse antiserum?

● Horse serum contains proteins unique to horses, which are recognised as 'non-self' by the human recipient's immune system. The increasingly powerful immune response to these proteins gradually destroys the horse antibodies, so passive protection from the antiserum declines. More seriously, the recipient's blood capillaries can become blocked by aggregates of human antibodies bound to horse proteins, triggering local inflammation and even kidney failure.

Although passive immunisation is now used infrequently due to the introduction of more effective chemotherapeutic agents and active vaccines, it was critically important in the past. For example, horse antiserum prevented thousands of deaths from tetanus among allied soldiers in World War I, and it can still be life-saving in some conditions.

Summary of Section 3.2

1   The majority of present-day vaccination programmes use active vaccines containing pathogen-specific antigens to elicit a protective immune response in the recipient. Repeated vaccination enhances the effectiveness of the antibody response and (for some vaccines) also elicits cell-mediated responses.

2   Passive immunisation uses antibodies raised in human donors or in horses, which are used either to treat certain life-threatening infections as soon as symptoms appear, or prophylactically to prevent infection after a known exposure.

3.3 Critical antigens and the immune response

> This section refers to how antibodies contribute to immune defences against infection; you may find it useful to revise Sections 2.1 and 2.4 of Book 3 briefly before reading on.

Before we consider vaccine design in more detail, it is necessary to point out that not all immune responses protect the host against the target pathogen. Consider antibody-mediated responses induced by a vaccine. Antigens that induce protective antibodies against pathogens (or their products) are known as **critical antigens**; so if vaccines are to elicit a protective or therapeutic antibody response they must contain pathogen-specific critical antigens.

○   Think back to the *Influenza* Case Study (Book 1, Chapter 2). What are the critical antigens of influenza A virus? Can you identify a flu antigen that is *not* critical? What distinguishes the critical antigens?

●   The haemagglutinin and neuraminidase are critical antigens included in all flu vaccines. They are involved in essential functions of the virus, namely getting into cells and getting out again. They are also the most prone to mutation (antigenic drift). Antibodies against them are protective because they are located on the outside of the virus and are therefore accessible to antibody-binding; by contrast, antibodies to the M-protein in the core are not protective.

The external coat of most viruses is relatively simple, since it contains a limited number of antigens, which can be targeted by the immune system. Polio virus has just three protein components exposed on the surface of its capsid (see Book 2, Figure 3.5). By contrast, bacteria are structurally more complex and generally induce antibodies against a variety of proteins. For example, purified protein derivative (PPD) is an antigenic preparation derived from mycobacteria, which contains up to 200 different antigens. Nevertheless, there are often a limited number of antigens which determine the pathogenicity of the bacteria. In extreme cases, such as tetanus, the toxin is the only relevant antigen that must be neutralised; the bacterium by itself is not invasive or particularly pathogenic, but the toxin is one of the most toxic substances known.

○   Explain how antibodies that bind to the critical antigens of a pathogen can protect the host from infection.

Antibodies are multi-purpose defensive molecules, whose functions include: preventing viruses from invading host cells by binding to their attachment sites; 'labelling' pathogens for destruction by cytotoxic cells and phagocytes; cross-linking pathogens into immobilised aggregates; directing the lytic complement pathway onto cellular pathogens; and recruiting other components of the immune response to fight an infection.

The pathogenicity of many bacteria depends on their ability to avoid phagocytosis by actively moving away from phagocytes, or by being encased in an anti-phagocytic capsule. Antibodies can overcome these defences. For example, by binding to critical antigens in the capsule they allow phagocytes to engage the bacteria (opsonisation, see Book 3, Section 2.1.6). Antibodies to flagella and other surface components reduce bacterial motility. Antibodies against bacterial enzymes such as collagenases, which promote the spread of streptococci and staphylococci, can also reduce the ability of these bacteria to invade tissues locally.

The critical antigens in some vaccines also induce cell-mediated immune responses in the recipient, which are particularly important in attacking pathogens that replicate inside host cells, i.e. all viruses and some bacteria, including mycobacteria (which cause TB and leprosy), and certain protoctist parasites (e.g. *Toxoplasma gondii*; *Plasmodium* species).

Summary of Section 3.3

1 Protective immune responses are directed against critical antigens in the pathogen's structure, or in its products (e.g. toxins, enzymes).

2 Antibodies that bind to critical antigens can neutralise or inhibit bacterial toxins and enzymes, immobilise pathogens, prevent them binding to host cells, and enhance their destruction by phagocytes and cytotoxic cells.

3.4 Strategies for vaccine production

The type of antigen preparation used in active vaccines varies considerably, depending on the pathogen. For diseases such as tetanus, where a bacterial toxin causes the damage, the toxin is first chemically treated to turn it into a harmless *toxoid*, which is used as the immunising agent. Where protection is required against the pathogen itself, vaccines are based on whole organisms treated in some way to make them safe, or on complex mixtures of antigens taken from the infectious agent. In this section, we discuss the major production strategies for active vaccines, which conventionally contain one or a combination of:

- *intact killed* pathogens;

- *live attenuated* pathogens;

- subcellular fragments or molecules from the pathogen – known as *subunit vaccines* – either alone or linked in 'conjugates' to other molecules.

Table 3.3 overleaf gives some examples of commonly used vaccines in each of these categories. The difficulties that can be encountered in developing an effective vaccine are well illustrated in Section 4.2 of the *Cholera* Case Study, which describes some of the many attempts to produce vaccines of all three types. Sometimes vaccine preparations consist of a mixture of components, as in one of the newer vaccines against cholera, which contains inactivated classical and El Tor bacterial strains and a component of the cholera toxin.

In addition, we will look briefly at a number of new approaches to vaccine design currently in development, including:

- *DNA vaccines* containing 'naked' DNA encoding specific pathogen antigens;

- Genetic engineering of genes coding for key pathogen antigens either as subunits, or for cloning into non-pathogenic infectious agents used as 'gene vectors' for expression in the vaccine recipient.

TABLE 3.3 Some examples of vaccine types.

Vaccine type	Infectious disease	Comments
killed or inactivated vaccines	polio	Salk vaccine (IPV, see *Polio* Case Study)
	cholera	various combinations of El Tor, classical Inaba and Ogawa serotypes (see *Cholera* Case Study)
	influenza	strains vary annually (see Book 1, Chapter 2)
	whooping cough	killed *Bordetella pertussis*
	typhoid	killed *Salmonella typhi*
	rabies	various strains with similar protection
live, attenuated vaccines	tuberculosis	Bacillus Calmette Guérin (BCG, see *TB* Case Study)
	typhoid	oral attenuated strain (Ty21a)
	polio	Sabin oral vaccine (OPV, see *Polio* Case Study)
	cholera	CVD103-HgR strain with attenuated El Tor strain
	measles, mumps and rubella	usually combined in MMR vaccine
	yellow fever	single strain, stable for decades
	chickenpox	attenuated varicella zoster (Oka strain)
subunit vaccines	tetanus	toxoid
	diphtheria	toxoid
	cholera	toxin A or B subunit (used in combination with killed or attenuated strains)
	meningococcal meningitis	Groups A and C surface polysaccharides; or conjugate vaccine (MenC)
	typhoid	capsular polysaccharide (Vi)
	pneumococcal pneumonia	combination of 23 variant surface polysaccharides
	haemophilus influenza	type B capsular polysaccharide; or conjugate Hib vaccine
	hepatitis B	surface antigen

3.4.1 Intact killed pathogens

The first deliberate attempts to create a **killed vaccine** were made by Louis Pasteur in 1885 (Figure 3.4). He took samples of brain and spinal cord from rabies-infected rabbits and inactivated the (then unknown) infective agent by drying the preparation, or by chemical treatment with formalin. Although many of Pasteur's vaccines were successful in inducing protective immunity, the methods of preparation often generated vaccines with unacceptably high levels of adverse reactions. For example, the rabies vaccine sometimes induced an *autoimmune* reaction in the central nervous system (CNS) of immunised subjects. The vaccine included molecules from the rabbit CNS, which led to a breakdown in some of its recipients of the normal tolerance to self-molecules found in the CNS. This occurred in only a small proportion of those immunised, but nevertheless the consequences could be fatal.

FIGURE 3.4
Louis Pasteur (left) depicted in a contemporary print, supervising the removal of rabies-infected rabbit brain and spinal cord to use in the preparation of the first rabies vaccine.

Many safe killed vaccines have since been produced using chemically inactivated or heat-killed pathogens, but effectiveness is highly variable. For example, the Salk vaccine (IPV) contains an inactivated preparation of the polio virus, which elicits a strong IgG response and long-lasting protection against paralytic polio; by comparison, killed *Vibrio cholerae* vaccines have generally produced limited immunity for a much shorter period (see the *Polio* and *Cholera* Case Studies).

☐ Both the Salk vaccine against polio and killed whole-cell cholera vaccines induce high levels of IgG antibodies. Why are IgG antibodies less useful against cholera than against polio?

▉ Polio virus must travel from the gut through the blood to the spinal cord before it can cause paralysis. Since IgG antibodies are the principal serum antibody, they can intercept the virus as it moves from one tissue to the other. In contrast, cholera produces its damage by attaching to cells in the gut epithelium, sometimes invading them, and by the release of enterotoxin. So IgG is of limited value in defence against cholera (IgA is much more important).

3.4.2 Attenuated pathogens

A major strategy for vaccine production has been the generation of attenuated organisms, which retain their antigenicity, but which have lost their pathogenicity. Generally speaking, **attenuated vaccines** containing killed organisms are *less* effective at inducing protective immunity than those using live attenuated strains.

⬜ Can you think of reasons why a live attenuated vaccine would be better at inducing an immune response than a killed version of the same pathogen?

⬤ The live organisms persist and reproduce for a period in the recipient, presenting a larger and more long-lasting stimulus to the immune system. Also the attenuated strain lives in the appropriate tissue of the host, so it is presented to the immune system by the correct antigen-presenting cells (see Book 3, Section 2.12.2).

In the earliest attempts, the method of producing attenuated strains was to grow the pathogen *in vitro*, or in laboratory animals over many generations, repeatedly testing to see whether the evolving strain had lost its pathogenicity. The first and most famous example was the strain of *Mycobacterium bovis* developed in France by Calmette and Guérin (Bacillus Calmette Guérin, BCG), which has been used since 1923 (see Table 3.1) as a vaccine against *M. tuberculosis*. Although data from BCG studies show highly variable levels of protection, this has been one of the most widely used of all vaccines – not least because it is cheap. However, it was only with the publication of the complete genome of *M. tuberculosis* in 1998 that it became clear exactly what the process of attenuation had done. Early in the development of the BCG strain, the bacteria lost a group of nine genes. Moreover, since the original preparation, different strains of BCG in laboratories in different parts of the world have continued to undergo further genetic diversification. Sequencing studies have also shown that *M. bovis* is quite closely related to *M. tuberculosis* over several areas of the genome, which explains why they share critical antigens recognised by the protective immune response.

The rationale for culturing a pathogen *in vitro* or in a non-human species is that it does not require some of its genes (perhaps for transmission, or spread within the body) and consequently these genes may be lost or mutated, (e.g. pox viruses only appear to require 70% of their genes to grow in mammalian cells). However, this process of attenuation has been described as 'genetic roulette', since there is no way of knowing what combination of genes will be lost or mutated and the process will produce different strains each time it is carried out.

The *Polio* Case Study illustrated another problem inherent in using attenuated strains – pathogenic reversion. The oral vaccine contains all three live polio strains in attenuated forms: although the type 1 strain has 57 mutations and has never reverted to the wild type, type 2 and type 3 each have only two relevant mutations, so they require only two reversions to become pathogenic again – as indeed has occurred on a number of occasions.

⬜ In general, it has proved easier to attenuate viruses than bacteria. Can you think of any reasons why this should be so?

It may be because most viruses are genetically less complex than bacteria and contain only a small number of genes, so a few mutations can result in attenuation of pathogenicity. Also most viruses mutate more quickly, so a variant with useful properties in a vaccine is likely to arise more frequently. Bacteria have a number of DNA repair mechanisms that are lacking in viruses, so they can correct or delete mutations that may otherwise have proved useful in a vaccine. Thus attenuation of pathogenicity in bacteria usually requires much larger genetic changes, but the loss of a segment of bacterial DNA often results in the loss of essential functions for life in addition to those for pathogenicity.

One of the most powerful arguments in favour of genetic engineering in vaccine production is that it can deliberately 'knock out' the gene sequences responsible for an organism's pathogenicity. The ability to manipulate pathogen genomes and their products is increasingly important in vaccine design, as we discuss below.

3.4.3 Subunit vaccines

The risk of pathogenic reversion can be overcome if the vaccine contains only fragments (subunits) of the pathogen, but these must include critical antigens in order to provoke a protective immune response. Relatively few **subunit vaccines** fulfil these criteria, but they include the inactivated toxins (toxoids) of tetanus and diphtheria which have been in use for many years. A subunit vaccine against whooping cough (Acellular Pertussis Vaccine, APV) is under evaluation. Antigen preparations for use in vaccines have also been made from structural components of certain bacteria and viruses, for example, a surface antigen from the hepatitis B virus, or the coat polysaccharides of *Neisseria meningitidis* or *Haemophilus influenzae*.

Since the 1990s, a few highly successful **conjugate vaccines** have been produced, in which a subunit from the target pathogen is irreversibly bound in a 'conjugate' with bacterial proteins. The conjugate elicits a greatly enhanced immune response compared with the subunit alone. Several effective conjugate vaccines against *H. influenzae* type b (Hib) are already in use. In 1999, the UK was the first country to introduce the conjugate MenC vaccine against meningitis caused by Group C meningococci. The vaccine contains a Group C polysaccharide subunit antigen conjugated with either a harmless variant of diphtheria toxin or the tetanus toxoid. Trials are also underway of a conjugate vaccine against genital herpes which links a herpes virus glycoprotein subunit with lipid A, a component of the Gram-negative bacterial envelope (see Book 2, Figures 2.6 and 2.7).

The components of subunit vaccines have until recently been extracted and purified from cultures of intact pathogens by conventional biochemical techniques, but there is now increasing research into the genetic engineering of critical antigens. If the genes encoding these antigens can be identified and isolated, they can be inserted into the genomes of harmless bacteria or yeasts (genetic recombination). The expression of these genes can yield commercially useful quantities of pathogen-specific antigens as components of **recombinant subunit vaccines**, such as the current hepatitis B vaccine; others are being evaluated (e.g. against herpes simplex and human papilloma viruses).

3.4.4 Vaccines of the future

Other applications of modern molecular biology in vaccine design are also coming into play, including **DNA vaccines**. The use of 'naked' (cell-free) DNA encoding critical antigens, directly injected into muscle, seems at first an improbable strategy, since the DNA does not have the necessary cellular machinery for its expression. Nevertheless, if the DNA has a suitable promoter, sufficient can be taken up by cells of the body to allow transcription and production of enough antigen to induce an immune response. The DNA construct is coated onto gold particles which are shot into the tissue using a gas-pressurised 'gene gun' (Figure 3.5). DNA vaccines have been tested in experimental animals with some success, inducing both antibodies and T-cell mediated immunity; trials of DNA constructs from HIV-1 and hepatitis B virus genomes have begun in human volunteers.

Another technique has been to produce genetically-engineered constructs in which the gene encoding a pathogen-specific critical antigen is transported into the vaccine recipient by a harmless virus or bacterium. These **vector vaccines** immunise the host against the critical antigen, which is expressed by the 'gene vector' (Figure 3.6).

Vaccinia is a popular choice as a gene vector, because it has a long history of relatively safe use in immunisation against smallpox and it can accommodate large amounts of DNA. Moreover, as the use of vaccinia for protection against smallpox has declined since the 1980s, the level of immunity to vaccinia in the population has fallen.

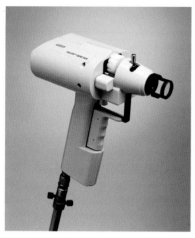

FIGURE 3.5

This gene gun uses a pulse of low pressure helium gas to deliver gold particles that have been coated with DNA or RNA directly into the tissues. (Courtesy of Bio-Rad)

○ Why is this important in designing a genetically-engineered vaccine assembled in vaccinia viruses?

▣ If the vaccine recipients are already immune to vaccinia, they would eliminate a vaccinia construct before it could induce immunity to the antigen it was carrying.

Several vector vaccines have been developed to combat HIV infection, so far with limited results. An early version used canarypox virus carrying genes for HIV surface proteins (gp120 and gp41) and encoding some internal molecules including the viral polymerase. (The structure of HIV is shown in Book 2, Figure 3.11 and in the HIV mini-lecture on *Immunology Interactive* CD2.) A strain of Venezuelan equine encephalitis virus (VEE) has also been used as a vector for gp120. VEE has the advantages of being able to infect human cells and express the HIV glycoprotein, and although it can replicate in human cells, it cannot produce infectious virions. Malaria is another priority target for development of vector vaccines using DNA constructs from *Plasmodium* carried in vaccinia or fowlpox viruses.

○ The examples given above all use gene vectors derived from non-human animal viruses: cowpox, canarypox, fowlpox and equine encephalitis. Why are these selected rather than a harmless virus that normally infects humans?

▣ Firstly, there is the consideration of safety. If a viral vector does not normally infect humans, then it is less likely to revert to a pathogenic type or exchange genetic information with a wild-type human virus. Secondly, recipients will be less likely to have prior immunity to a non-human virus, which would interfere with the development of immunity to the critical antigen in the vaccine.

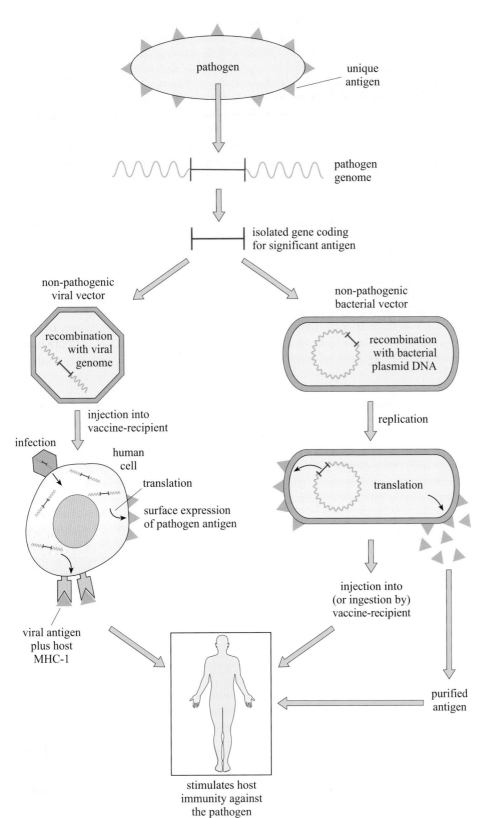

FIGURE 3.6
Vector vaccines can be produced using harmless viruses or bacterial strains to carry genes encoding pathogen-specific antigens, which are expressed in the vaccine recipient and stimulate host immunity against the pathogen.

Bacteria are also under investigation as gene vectors (Figure 3.6), for example, in the oral typhoid vaccine, Ty21a. There are certain advantages in this approach: bacteria that live in the gut tend to induce strong immune responses in the gut-associated lymphoid tissues (GALT), including a good IgA response. Thus, bacterial vectors that express the antigens they are carrying in the gut would generate the type of immune response required to combat the enteric bacteria and viruses that cause diarrhoeal diseases. At the time of writing (2003) no bacterial constructs have been licensed for mass vaccination in humans, but Ty21a is being tested as a vector for a variety of bacterial and other antigens, and the first human trial of HIV genes in a bacterial vector has begun.

Finally, an interesting development has been the insertion of single genes encoding critical antigens from bacteria and viruses into plant genomes, including those of potatoes and tomatoes. The antigens are expressed in the plant, which can then be eaten with the aim of inducing an immune response in the gut! The first trial of an **oral plant vaccine** against hepatitis B virus using genetically engineered potatoes began in the USA in 1999. If it turns out to be protective, it would have a significant effect in developing countries where viral hepatitis is a major health problem. Growing anti-HBV potatoes for local consumption would be a cheap and effective way of protecting the population.

○ What could limit the efficacy of oral plant vaccines?

◉ Most proteins in foods are broken down by digestive enzymes in the stomach and intestine, so the critical antigens may be destroyed before they can elicit an immune response. Even if they survive digestion, most people do not usually produce immune responses to antigens in foods, perhaps because food antigens do not induce costimulatory signals for T and B cells (Book 3, Section 2.9.1, see under 'Costimulation', particularly Figure 2.33).

Figure 3.7 summarises the current gene-based approaches to vaccine development.

In addition to the pragmatic question of whether a genetically engineered vaccine will induce protective immunity, there is a debate as to whether it is safe to produce such vaccines at all. The arguments are ranged along lines that have been well-rehearsed in more general concerns about genetic engineering. Critics think that altering infectious agents – albeit harmless ones – could produce pathogenic reversion, or further unplanned recombination of the vaccine vector with other bacteria or viruses to produce pathogenic strains. Proponents think that this risk can be made negligible by comprehensively disabling the vectors. The debate is difficult to resolve because although the risks and dangers of contracting an infectious disease are quantified, the risks and dangers from a new genetic vaccine are hypothetical. Other issues of vaccine safety are discussed in Section 3.8.

Summary of Section 3.4

1   Conventional vaccines contain either killed pathogens or attenuated strains (live or killed) with the same critical antigens as the target pathogen. Genetic manipulation may delete the genes involved in pathogenicity to create new attenuated strains.

2   Subunit vaccines contain pathogen fragments extracted by conventional biochemical techniques, or genetically engineered constructs. The subunit

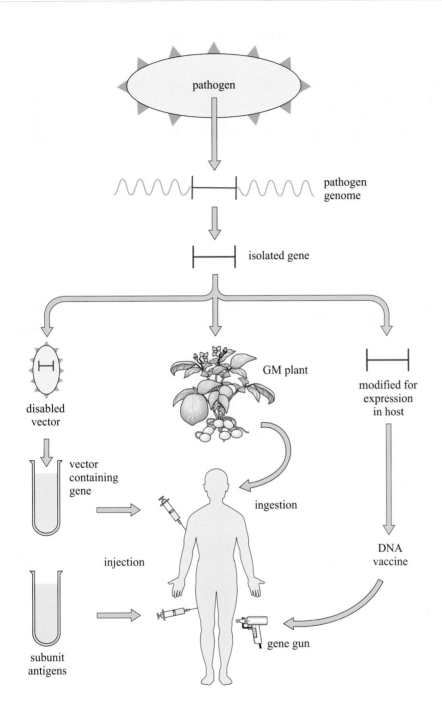

FIGURE 3.7
Genetic approaches to vaccine development. One or more genes encoding critical pathogen-specific antigens are isolated and recombined with a harmless or disabled vector for delivery by injection, or incorporated into food plants for ingestion, or modified for injection as naked DNA. subunit antigens can be produced by genetic engineering.

antigen may be conjugated with bacterial proteins or lipids to enhance its ability to induce protective immunity.

3   DNA vaccines contain naked DNA encoding a pathogen-specific antigen which is 'fired' into host tissues and expressed there; vector vaccines contain pathogen genes inserted into the genomes of harmless viruses or bacteria. Both vaccine types generate an immune response when the gene product is expressed in the recipient. Oral plant vaccines are genetically engineered to express pathogen antigens with the aim of eliciting protective immunity in the gut when eaten.

3.5 Influences on vaccine efficacy

This section refers to the discussion of vaccine efficacy in Book 6, Chapter 4. You may also find it useful to look back briefly at Book 3, Section 1.2.3 on antigen-presenting cells, Section 2.5.4 on antigen-presentation by macrophages, and Section 2.9.1 on the major histocompatibility complex (MHC) molecules. As you do so, focus on how these cells and molecules influence the type and effectiveness of the immune response to an antigen.

As Book 6 explained, the efficacy of a protective vaccine is rarely 100%. Vaccine efficacy can be calculated from the *secondary attack rates* in vaccinated and unvaccinated individuals and expressed as the relative reduction in the risk of infection in vaccine recipients, compared to the risk in unvaccinated people. In this section, we discuss factors that influence vaccine efficacy and determine whether it reaches the level required to protect a recipient against subsequent infection. We are not concerned here with population effects such as herd immunity and critical immunization thresholds, which influence the ability of a vaccination programme to eliminate an infection in a community (we consider this in Section 3.7).

3.5.1 Antigens and immunogens

In Section 3.3 we highlighted the need for vaccines to contain pathogen-specific *critical antigens*, which provoke a protective immune response. Clearly, a vaccine that did not contain critical antigens would be ineffective, but we must now extend the discussion to include other influences on vaccine efficacy. We noted above that pathogens can have antigens that do not induce a protective immune response and that (in most people) antigens in foods do not elicit immunity at all. This introduces an important concept in immunology. It is necessary to distinguish between **antigenicity**, the ability of a molecule to be recognised as non-self by the cells of the immune system – and **immunogenicity**, the ability of that antigen to induce an immune response. Immunogenicity is not a fixed property: whether a particular antigen behaves as an immunogen is highly contingent on a number of interacting factors, including:

- the route by which it is delivered (e.g. orally; injected into the skin; inhaled intranasally); and the quantity of antigen in the 'dose';

- the genetic make-up of the immunised person and how this affects the ability to make an immune response to a particular antigen;

- the molecular structure of the antigen (e.g. carbohydrate, protein, lipid);

- the presence of other molecules that enhance immune responsiveness.

☐ How could the route of administration influence the kind of immune response that develops against the antigens in a vaccine?

⬤ Different parts of the body have different antigen-presenting cells, and this determines how an antigen is presented and what kinds of T cells are stimulated.

Antigen presentation partly determines whether a T helper-1 (T_H1) or a T helper-2 (T_H2) type of response is favoured. Antigens presented to T_H1 cells initiate the sequence of events culminating in cell-mediated immune responses; antigens presented to TH2 cells initiate antibody-mediated responses. In practice, both types of response can occur simultaneously, but the route of administration can favour one or the other. It can also influence the class of antibodies that appear: antigens presented in the gut will tend to induce IgA production, since large numbers of IgA-producing B cells are located there; by contrast, antigens injected into the skin will usually be transported to local lymph nodes, where IgG- and IgM-producing B cells predominate.

☐ Explain how the genetic make-up of an individual can affect antigen presentation and why this has an influence on whether a vaccine is immunogenic.

◉ Antigen-presenting cells take up the vaccine antigens, process them internally and present peptide fragments in the cleft of their own surface MHC class II molecules. The genes encoding the MHC molecules vary between individuals, producing variations in which peptides can be presented to other cells in the immune system. Different individuals will present some protein antigens more efficiently than others. Inefficient antigen-presentation means that these antigens may be less immunogenic *in that individual*, even though they may provoke a strongly protective immune response in individuals with a different set of MHC class II molecules.

☐ What implication does this have for vaccine design?

◉ The variation in MHC molecules in a population means that the antigens used in vaccines must be presented efficiently in genetically different individuals.

In addition to the MHC, several other gene loci have been identified that affect the ability to generate a protective immune response; these include genes that affect antigen processing, as well as those involved in cytokine production and cell/cell interactions.

The molecular structure of an antigen can also affect whether it is immunogenic and the type of immune response it generates. Carbohydrates, lipids and glycolipid antigens are processed differently to protein antigens and they are not presented by conventional MHC molecules; for example, glycolipids are presented by a surface molecule designated CD1 (see Book 3, Section 2.9.1, under 'Antigen presentation by non-classical MHC molecules'). Carbohydrates do not generally induce antibody class-switching, so they do not induce the production of high affinity IgG antibodies. We shall not go further into the details of how non-protein antigens are handled by the immune system, but you should note that it is essential that vaccines induce a strong, effective and long-lasting immune response to certain carbohydrates and glycolipids.

☐ Can you explain why?

◉ The surface of many bacteria consists of carbohydrates and glycolipids, and an effective antibody response against them is highly desirable.

The immunogenicity of pathogen antigens is thus essential to vaccine design, but this is often hard to achieve; for example, some critical antigens are not sufficiently immunogenic in a wide enough range of individuals. However, various other components of the vaccine preparation can be added to enhance the immune response. Such components are called adjuvants.

3.5.2 Adjuvants

Adjuvants are components of vaccines that enhance their immunogenic potential. In general, they work in one of two ways:

1   They concentrate the antigen in one place (the 'depot effect').

2   They activate antigen-presenting cells and induce cytokine production (Figure 3.8).

The first adjuvants to be devised used antigens in emulsions with aluminium salts, which created depots of antigen and greatly enhanced the levels of antibodies produced in response. Aluminium hydroxide is still added to some vaccines for use in humans, including the diphtheria and tetanus toxoids. Work in animals showed that emulsions containing killed mycobacteria were exceptionally good at producing strong immune responses to other antigens. Mycobacterial products are very effective at activating macrophages and these adjuvants are thought to act by enhancing antigen presentation.

○   How can bacterial products enhance antigen presentation by macrophages?

●   Macrophages have receptors for a variety of bacterial components (including lipopolysaccharide, LPS). Receptor binding to these components causes increased expression of MHC molecules and costimulatory molecules on the macrophage surface, and enhanced secretion of stimulatory cytokines such as IL-1 and TNFα. This upregulation increases the efficiency with which macrophages present antigens to T cells and stimulate T cell activation.

Some bacterial components such as LPS produce adverse local reactions in human recipients, which prevent their use in human vaccines. For example, mycobacteria can cause severe ulceration of the skin, especially in people who have been previously sensitised to them. However, these problems have been overcome in the newer conjugate vaccines (described earlier), which link the antigen irreversibly to

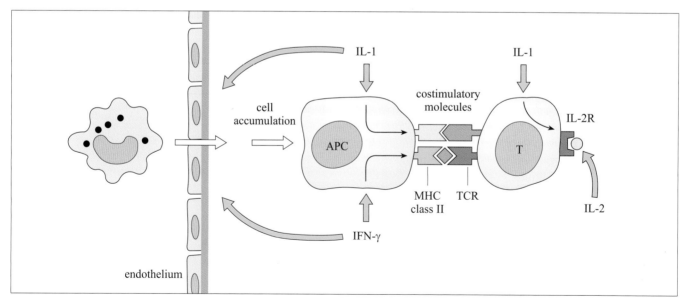

FIGURE 3.8 Cytokines with potential applications as adjuvants in vaccines. Both IL-1 and IFN-γ cause leukocytes to be attracted to and accumulate at a source of antigen, e.g. a vaccine injection site. IL-1 increases the expression of costimulatory molecules on antigen-presenting cells (APCs) and IL-2 receptors (Il-2R) on T cells. IFN-γ increases the expression of MHC molecules and costimulatory molecules on APCs. IL-2 is required for T-cell division, so it enhances cell-mediated immunity.

bacterial products such as diphtheria or tetanus toxoid, or lipid A. Another technique is to use liposomes, microscopic sacs formed from phospholipids, which trap antigens and ensure that they can be taken up in quantity by antigen-presenting cells. In general, these adjuvants act via the depot effect.

The second category of adjuvants takes a different approach, by incorporating cytokines into the vaccine to enhance the immune response directly. At present (2003) this strategy has been tried in experimental animals, principally using IL-1, IL-2 and IFN-γ, but none have yet been approved for use in vaccines for humans. Figure 3.8 summarises how these cytokines should (in theory) enhance immune responses to vaccines, although there are many difficulties to be overcome, including the high cost of producing synthetic cytokines.

Summary of Section 3.5

1 When designing a vaccine, the antigens it contains must be immunogenic and selected to induce a protective immune response in genetically different recipients.

2 The molecular structure of the antigen, the route of administration and the presence of adjuvants in the vaccine can all influence the efficacy of the immune response, and the type and location of antibody-mediated and cell-mediated defences.

3 Adjuvants in vaccines function either by concentrating antigen in 'depots' where they are more effectively taken up by antigen-presenting cells, or by stimulating components of the immune response directly.

> You should now go to the mini-lecture entitled 'Vaccination' on *Immunology* CD2. It reviews and consolidates many of the concepts presented in Sections 3.2 to 3.5 of this chapter, using diphtheria and polio vaccines as examples. Spend about 30 minutes on this activity.

3.6 Challenges to vaccine development

Vaccination seems such a straightforward and effective strategy for controlling infectious disease that the question arises of why we cannot develop vaccines against every pathogen and parasite.

○ Suggest reasons why effective vaccines already exist (a) against polio, but not against HIV infection; (b) against influenza, but not the common cold; and (c) against tetanus, but not syphilis.

● (a) Polio virus is genetically fairly stable, so the organism does not mutate and there are only three strains to be included in the vaccine. In contrast, the surface molecules of HIV mutate so quickly that antigenic drift occurs continuously even within a single infected individual, making a vaccine extremely difficult to design. And we have yet to discover what would be an effective immune response against HIV.

(b) At any one time there are only a few strains of influenza virus in circulation, so although current vaccines only protect recipients against known strains, the emergence of vaccine-resistant virus is a relatively rare occurrence. Compare this with the viruses that causes colds, of which there are more than 100 in circulation. Moreover influenza is a much more serious illness than the common cold, so there is much more incentive to develop a vaccine against it.

(c) Tetanus presents a well-defined target for the immune response, since we know that antibodies against the toxoid will neutralise it; in contrast we are mostly ignorant of what constitutes an effective immune response against the spirochaetes that cause syphilis.

Comparisons such as these reveal that the factors limiting vaccination strategies to control infectious diseases fall into five broad categories.

1   *The nature of the pathogen*: including, its distribution in human populations and whether it infects non-human hosts; its mode and speed of transmission; the type of symptoms it causes; whether the disease has a symptom-free latent period or a 'carrier' state.

2   *The nature of the immune response*: including, whether antibody-mediated or cell-mediated immunity predominates in an effective immune response; the type and location of protective responses; the identification and immunogenicity of critical antigens; scientific knowledge of how to enhance the immune response.

3   *Economic factors*: including, whether it is cost-effective to develop a vaccine and whether a vaccine would be affordable by those who would benefit most from it.

4   *Organisational factors*: including, whether the infrastructure and personnel necessary to conduct a vaccination programme exist in a susceptible population.

5   *Cultural factors*: including, the level of public understanding of what vaccination can (and cannot) protect against, and concerns about vaccine safety.

These categories cannot be considered in isolation from each other: as Book 5 demonstrated, the co-evolution of pathogens and their hosts means that (1) and (2) above are intrinsically related and continuously changing; the state of scientific knowledge of the pathogen and host immune responses influence whether (3) the economic case will favour research into a new vaccine; an effective vaccine may be produced, but organisational difficulties (4) may mean that it cannot be delivered where it is most needed (e.g. due to lack of refrigerated storage facilities or trained vaccinators); and (5) concerns about safety may limit vaccine uptake.

In the rest of this section, we consider *biological* factors of the pathogen and the host, which present challenges to the development of vaccines. In Section 3.7, we turn to the economic, organisational and cultural limitations on vaccination as a strategy to control infectious disease.

3.6.1 Zoonoses

Eradication of a disease is a splendid aim, but although vaccines exist against some important zoonotic diseases (e.g. tuberculosis), this goal is extremely difficult or even impossible to achieve for zoonoses. The situation is well illustrated by the viral zoonoses such as yellow fever. An effective vaccine has been available against yellow fever virus for several decades, but the WHO estimates there are still at least 200 000 cases per year with 30 000 deaths (WHO, 2001). The virus is present in monkeys in equatorial Africa and South America and is transmitted from monkeys to humans principally by mosquito bite. It is clearly impossible to eradicate the virus, because there is a very large natural host population of monkeys in which it will persist. Also, the female mosquitoes can transmit the virus 'vertically' to their offspring in their eggs, maintaining its presence in the vector population.

Over 200 viruses fall into the category of zoonotic infections (Taylor, 2001), including some of the most lethal human infections ever identified. They include Lassa fever, Hanta virus pulmonary syndrome, Ebola fever and Marburg disease. Fortunately, the incidence of human infection with these diseases is still very low and usually sporadic, but case fatality levels are typically 50–80% (as Figure 3.9 illustrates). In epidemics, human-to-human transmission readily occurs among close contacts of the original case, but strict quarantine measures have (so far) contained the outbreaks, although complete control has sometimes taken over a year. Nevertheless, the episodic recurrence shown in Figure 3.9 demonstrates the potential dangers of a large pool of 'animal' viruses, either transmitting infection to humans directly or acting as a source for the development of new human viruses.

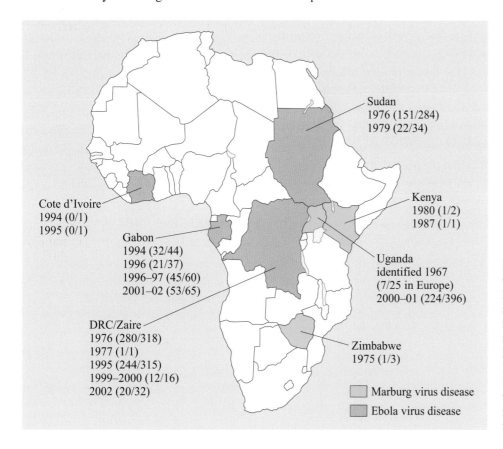

Cote d'Ivoire
1994 (0/1)
1995 (0/1)

Gabon
1994 (32/44)
1996 (21/37)
1996–97 (45/60)
2001–02 (53/65)

DRC/Zaire
1976 (280/318)
1977 (1/1)
1995 (244/315)
1999–2000 (12/16)
2002 (20/32)

Sudan
1976 (151/284)
1979 (22/34)

Kenya
1980 (1/2)
1987 (1/1)

Uganda
identified 1967
(7/25 in Europe)
2000–01 (224/396)

Zimbabwe
1975 (1/3)

Marburg virus disease
Ebola virus disease

FIGURE 3.9
Outbreaks of Marburg disease and Ebola fever in Africa, 1970s to 2002, showing the year and (in brackets) the number of fatalities as a fraction of the number of clinically identified cases. Marburg virus was first identified in 1967 when staff at scientific institutes in Marburg, Frankfurt and Belgrade were infected by research material from African green monkeys imported from Uganda.

Although it would be desirable to have vaccines against high-fatality viral zoonoses, the animal reservoirs of infection will always be present. Moreover, there are a number of other factors which mean that vaccine development is of relatively low priority. Firstly, if the disease is very rare, the financial incentive for a company to develop a vaccine is lacking. Secondly, there are such a large number of zoonotic viruses that it is difficult to know where to start. An individual who is planning to travel in an area where the infections are found might have to be immunised against a wide range of viruses. Despite these factors, some vaccine development is underway for viral haemorrhagic diseases, since they would be of particular value to health care workers involved in controlling epidemics.

3.6.2 Asymptomatic carriers

A related problem for disease eradication is seen in some human infectious diseases, where a **carrier state** develops. One example is typhoid, where 2–5% of individuals become chronically infected, but without any symptoms of the disease. They excrete the typhoid bacteria continuously into their faeces and act as a persistent reservoir of infection. There have been several notable instances of individuals whose work involved food preparation, who have unwittingly passed the disease to dozens of others via the faecal–oral route.

Another example is the hepatitis B virus (HBV), the major cause of progressive liver disease and hepatic cancers worldwide, which can exist in an asymptomatic carrier state. About two billion people worldwide are infected with HBV, of whom 350 million are carriers. Very rarely, health workers in the UK are discovered to be carriers of HBV when they accidentally infect patients. (Medical students in the UK and people who come into contact with human tissue are usually vaccinated against HBV.) The majority of cases of HBV infection in Western countries are now either sexually transmitted or related to intravenous drug-use; the virus can also be transmitted vertically and post-natal transmission from mother to baby is the principal route in South-East Asia.

3.6.3 Evasion of the immune response

This section refers to some pathogen 'escape' mechanisms discussed in detail in Book 3, Section 5.2, and in the 'Trypanosomiasis' and 'Malaria' mini-lectures on *Immunology Interactive* CD2. It would be useful to review this material now if you have time.

All the infectious agents that cause disease in humans have had to evolve ways of evading our immune responses. Even the zoonoses which have other hosts, and diseases such as tetanus and cholera with causative agents that live in the environment in a free-living form, have adapted to survive for at least a period in human hosts.

Some pathogens mutate or change their surface molecules so rapidly that they keep 'one step ahead' of the immune response, at least for a time; some disguise themselves from recognition by the immune system; and others have developed ways of limiting the effectiveness of the mechanisms directed against them.

○ Give examples of pathogens that evade immune responses by: (a) antigenic variation; (b) antigenic disguise; and (c) countermeasures against immune effector mechanisms.

● (a) Influenza virus and HIV, malarial parasites and trypanosomes all undergo rapid antigenic variation. (b) Schistosomes 'cloak' themselves with host proteins, disguising their own surface antigens; herpes viruses and pox viruses appear to have incorporated host genes into their own genomes, enabling them

to produce proteins that inactivate the complement lytic pathway.
(c) Mycobacteria synthesise proteins that inhibit fusion between the lysosomes containing destructive oxygen intermediates and the phagosomes in which they enter the host cell; staphylococci and streptococci have receptors for antibody Fc regions, which compete with Fc receptors on macrophages – the bacteria 'trap' the antibodies so they cannot opsonise the bacteria for destruction by the macrophages. (There are many other examples; see Book 3, Section 5.2.)

Some additional points about antigenic variation are worth considering in the context of vaccine design. One of the greatest challenges to vaccine development comes from pathogens that mutate their surface antigens very rapidly. In many cases, the areas that mutate are those on exposed loops of external proteins. In HIV, for example, mutation of specific parts of the pathogen's structure can contribute to evasion of the immune response without interfering with the structural integrity of the virus. There are specific regions on gp120, the large surface glycoprotein of HIV, which are particular targets for antibody responses (i.e. they are immunogenic). These regions are particularly susceptible to mutation, so their shapes 'drift' as the antibody response builds up, and new clones of B cells have to be activated to cope with the change. However, these immunogenic regions are not vital functional areas of the gp120 molecule. As the gp120 molecule is required by the virus for attachment to CD4 on helper T cells and macrophages, it cannot mutate randomly since it must always retain its ability to bind to CD4. It is notable that the areas that mutate the most are *outside* the CD4-binding site.

A different kind of problem is seen in trypanosomes, which switch their variant surface glycoproteins (VSGs; see the 'Trypanosomiasis' mini-lecture on *Immunology* CD2). The sole function of these molecules is to protect the outer surface of the parasite and deflect the antibody response. Although immune responses are effective for a time against one VSG, they are ultimately ineffective in controlling the progression of the disease. There are invariant proteins on the trypanosome surface, but these are much less prevalent and less immunogenic than the VSGs, so they are useless as components of a vaccine. One of the main aims of vaccine designers, therefore, is to induce immune responses to those segments of critical antigens that are constrained and cannot mutate without the pathogen losing a key function.

A related problem arises with malaria. The antigens of *Plasmodium* are extremely complex and vary between different stages of the life cycle of the parasite. Some proteins vary between different *Plasmodium* strains, while others are relatively constant. An example is the circumsporozoite (CS) antigen, which is involved in attachment of the *Plasmodium* sporozoite to host liver cells. More than half of the CS protein consists of simple repeats of four amino acids (Figure 3.10 overleaf). Such an area may be immunogenic, while being unimportant for protein function.

○ Explain how other 'decoy' proteins of the malaria parasite protect it from host antibody-mediated responses and why they present a challenge for vaccine design; (recall the 'Malaria' mini-lecture on *Immunology* CD2).

● Several proteins act as decoys by detaching from the parasite's surface or from the surface of infected red cells. Antibodies against these proteins do not direct an immune response against the parasite itself, and they are 'mopped up' by binding to the decoy proteins. Including these proteins in a vaccine would induce the production of antibodies that were similarly ineffective.

The existence of all these escape mechanisms means that it takes a considerable time for even partial immunity to malaria to develop in a naturally-infected population. Consequently, it has been difficult to identify exactly which immune responses would be effective against the parasite, and what to include in a vaccine that could stimulate protective response mechanisms.

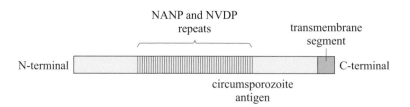

FIGURE 3.10 Schematic representation of the circumsporozoite (CS) antigen of *Plasmodium falciparum* strain IMT22. The highlighted area contains 37 repeats of the amino-acid sequence asparagine-alanine-asparagine-proline (known as NANP), and 4 repeats of the sequence asparagine-valine-aspartate-proline (or NVDP). The number of repeats and their arrangement vary greatly between different parasite strains.

3.6.4 Multiple strains

A similar problem for vaccine design comes from those pathogens that exist in a very large number of different 'strains' which are in circulation concurrently. The individual strains are generally stable, so it is not the case (as with rapid mutation and antigenic drift) that new strains are arising all the time, but the numbers of different strains that would need to be included in a vaccine is immense. For example, the streptococci that cause disease in humans can be classified into 20 main serotypes and more than 100 subtypes, based on recognition by specific antibodies. (For methods of identification of bacterial strains by serological and other techniques, see Book 4, Section 2.3.2. and Chapter 3.) Salmonella bacteria exist in over 2200 different serotypes! This makes it very difficult to design a vaccine that can induce protection against even a significant number of these strains. Apart from the basic problem of identifying and culturing the relevant strains, if too many are included in the vaccine, then the amount of each is too low to induce an adequate immune response. At present, satisfactory vaccines exist for only a few of the pathogenic salmonellae or streptococcal bacteria.

3.6.5 Prion diseases

Finally, we should look at the particular problems associated with prion diseases, or *transmissible spongiform encephalopathies* (TSEs; see Book 2, Chapter 4), such as variant Creutzfeld Jacob Disease (vCJD) and kuru. Prion diseases are caused by altered forms (prions) of small membrane glycoproteins, which are normally expressed on a number of cell types in the body, including neurons and lymphocytes. Once prions have appeared, the endogenous protein becomes folded in the same conformation as the prion, so the prions appear to 'replicate' and act like an infectious agent.

☐   Why will it be very difficult to develop a vaccine against prion diseases?

● The prion protein has the same primary amino-acid structure as the endogenous protein, so it is perceived as a 'self-molecule' by T cells and an immune response cannot develop.

In theory, the conformational differences between the prion and the endogenous protein might allow it to be recognised by B cells and antibodies, because they recognise the overall shape (conformation) of an antigen. However, in practice any differences seem to be too small to be immunogenic, possibly since the B cells do not receive help from T cells.

3.6.6 Conclusion

Where pathogens show great antigenic variation or multiple strains, the problems of vaccine development revolve around difficulties in identifying critical antigens that show little variation and which induce protective immunity. The challenge to achieve this has not yet been met for a number of important infectious diseases, which still lack effective vaccines (Table 3.4). Nevertheless, with the possible exception of prions, there are no theoretical reasons why vaccines cannot be developed to give protection against most infectious diseases. However, the limitations on vaccination strategies extend beyond the challenges posed by incomplete biological knowledge – as the final section of this chapter illustrates.

TABLE 3.4 Some examples of infections that cannot yet be controlled by vaccination. †

Pathogen	Examples	Disease	Problem with vaccine design
helminths	*Schistosoma* species	schistosomiasis	antigenic disguise with host proteins
protoctists	*Plasmodium* species	malaria	antigenic variation and morphological complexity
	Trypanosoma species	sleeping sickness	extreme antigenic variation
fungi	*Pneumocystis*	fungal pneumonia	ignorance of effective immunity
	Candida	thrush	ignorance of effective immunity
bacteria	*Streptococci*	skin and throat infections	multiple serotypes
	Treponema pallidum	syphilis	ignorance of effective immunity
viruses	HIV	AIDS	antigenic variation
	'cold' viruses	common cold	many different types of unrelated virus
prions	vCJD prions	variant Creutzfeldt-Jakob disease	lack of immunogenicity

† Many other infectious diseases can only be partially controlled by vaccines with low efficacy (e.g. cholera).

Summary of Section 3.6

Features of host-pathogen interactions that present a major challenge to vaccine development include:

1 A permanent reservoir of infection in other animals (zoonoses) or in carrier individuals, and free-living pathogens in the environment.

2 Rapid mutation of pathogen genomes resulting in antigenic variation, antigenic disguise with host proteins, multiple strains, or different antigens at different stages of the pathogen's life cycle.

3   Effective countermeasures in pathogens to evade or inhibit immune responses against them including decoy proteins, and inhibition of lysosome fusion complement activation or antigen presentation.

4   Immunogenic regions located away from regions that are essential for pathogen survival and replication.

5   Weak or absent immunogenicity of pathogen antigens, which also creates scientific uncertainty about what constitutes an effective immune response.

3.7 Limitations on vaccination programmes

This section refers back to the estimation of vaccine efficacy, herd immunity and critical immunization thresholds in Book 6, Chapter 4. You could usefully revise this material before reading on.

Where vaccination programmes have been successful, they have been immensely powerful and effective ways of combating infectious disease. Following the eradication of smallpox, a number of other diseases, including polio, mumps and rubella (German measles) are in line for global eradication over the next 10–20 years. Vaccines could, in theory, be developed for a larger range of infectious diseases than is currently the case, but there are complex economic, organisational and cultural limitations on vaccination programmes that are not easy to disentangle. Some of the major reasons why some diseases are apparently 'neglected' as candidates for vaccine control are discussed in this final section; you will readily identify other limitations on vaccination programmes when you conduct an Internet search into their progress at the end of this chapter.

3.7.1 Cost-effectiveness

The lack of a vaccine against certain infectious agents may not be because the scientific knowledge of the pathogen or the host is inadequate, but because it would not be cost-effective to develop one. At first sight, this may seem surprising, given that most vaccines are generally very cheap and effective. The Global Alliance for Vaccines and Immunisations (GAVI, a consortium of international health agencies, charities, governments and pharmaceutical companies formed in 1999) supplies the DTP vaccine against diphtheria, tetanus and pertussis (whooping cough), the oral polio vaccine, the combined MMR measles, mumps and rubella vaccine, and the BCG vaccine against tuberculosis, to immunise children in developing countries at a cost of under US$1 per dose. In addition, there is the cost of organising, conducting and evaluating a mass vaccination programme. Nevertheless, the cost per person for the most widely used vaccines is small – particularly when set against the estimated two million children who still die each year from vaccine-preventable diseases.

However, not all vaccines are cheap: some are priced above the means of the countries that need them most and supplies may not be sufficient to meet demand. For example, 12 million doses of a vaccine against all four of the major strains of meningococcal bacteria are sold to rich countries every year at differential prices, ranging up to US$50 a dose in the USA. An offer by the manufacturers to supply 2 million doses to African countries at $2.75 each was more than they could afford and far below the 10 million doses required (*Lancet Infectious Diseases* Newsdesk, 2002).

The major expense comes in the initial stages of laboratory research to develop a new vaccine, and particularly in conducting the clinical trials required to establish whether it is safe and effective (Box 3.1). This cost may be over US$150 million when all expenses are included. Commercial companies take strategic decisions as to whether such investment can be justified in relation to the returns available. The urgent work to develop HIV vaccines has been driven partly by the fact that an estimated 1.5 million people in the USA and Western Europe were living with HIV infection by the end of 2001, causing over 27 000 deaths annually. (Global and regional HIV/AIDS data are regularly updated on the WHO websites listed in the *Course Resources* section of the course website.) Given that over 90% of AIDS deaths occur in poor countries, the extent to which HIV affects the rich countries of the world, where citizens would pay a lot for a protective vaccine, has been a factor in the race to develop the first one. But the world market of 6 billion people (since everyone is at risk from HIV) is the greatest possible incentive to investors, and hundreds of millions of dollars have been committed to research into protective and therapeutic HIV vaccines. (For reports on progress, see links to the International AIDS Vaccine Initiative website under *Course Resources*.)

BOX 3.1   Clinical trials of vaccines

After extensive laboratory tests on animals, **clinical trials** of vaccine efficacy and safety take place in humans in three phases (mirroring the clinical trials of new medicines described in Chapter 2). Phase 1 trials assess the tolerability of the vaccine in a small number of healthy volunteers. Phase 2 trials test various vaccination regimens (dosage, spacing) for efficacy and tolerability in well-defined groups of a few hundred individuals who are at high risk of infection (e.g. in the case of HIV vaccine trials, the recipients have included injecting-drug users and sex workers). Effects of the vaccine on their immune responses are evaluated and the subsequent rate of infection in the vaccinees is compared with that in control groups who received placebo (dummy) vaccinations, or the existing vaccine where the trial is of a newer preparation. Phase 2 trials of *therapeutic* vaccines may also be conducted on already-infected subjects, to see if the vaccine slows the progression of the disease or has adverse effects (e.g. promoting a damaging inflammatory response). Phase 3 trials involve large groups of uninfected people (usually thousands) and may have a 'multi-centre' design, with different research teams evaluating the outcomes in different locations (see Figure 3.11). During the Phase 3 trials, attempts will be made to get the vaccine registered for use in the countries in which the first vaccination programme is to be launched. Thereafter, the performance of the vaccine is monitored in mass vaccination programmes in the target populations.

FIGURE 3.11
Parents in Southern India queue for their children to be vaccinated during a trial of a new vaccine against leprosy, 1990.

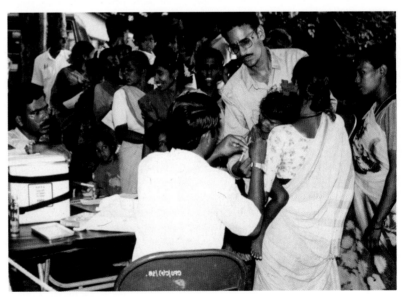

The prospect of lucrative markets in high-income countries has undoubtedly driven research into protective vaccines against human papilloma virus infection, a major contributory factor in cervical cancers, and into the development of a therapeutic vaccine that directs the immune system to destroy the 'plaques and tangles' in the brains of people with Alzheimer's disease. By comparison, resources for developing vaccines against parasite-mediated diseases, such as Chagas' disease and sleeping sickness, which only affect poorer countries, have been comparatively meagre. In some cases the veterinary significance of a zoonotic pathogen or parasite may be given higher priority and this can initiate research into a vaccine that translates subsequently into a preparation for human usage.

Governments, charities and non-commercial organisations also take decisions on the relative merits of vaccines compared with other, more cost-effective, control measures. For example, syphilis is readily treated by antibiotics and the spirochaete has not become antibiotic resistant. Since most antibiotics are also cheap and even easier to administer than vaccines, there have been few incentives to develop a vaccine against syphilis. A similar argument has applied to many other bacterial diseases, such as streptococcal infections and gonorrhoea. However, with the increase in antibiotic resistance in many important bacterial pathogens, the balance of the argument is now shifting towards vaccine development.

For some infectious diseases – particularly the diarrhoeal diseases and those caused by parasites – the public health strategies outlined in Chapter 1 may be as (or more) effective than vaccination. For example, the provision of clean drinking water and sanitation has done more to prevent epidemics of cholera than has any vaccination programme. We shall consider 'non-medical' controls (i.e. not based on medicines or vaccines) in Chapters 4 and 5, in the wider context of public health interventions against infectious diseases.

3.7.2 Organisational difficulties

As the *Polio* Case Study illustrated, the attempt to eradicate a major infectious disease requires an immense effort to organise systematic vaccination programmes throughout all endemic regions, backed up by vigilance to identify residual areas where the pathogen may be persisting or could have been re-introduced. Mass vaccination programmes present a huge logistical task for those who are engaged in their organisation and delivery. Consider what must be involved in administering the National Immunisation Days (NIDs), which aim to vaccinate several million children concurrently at hundreds of centres throughout countries such as India, Somalia or Peru.

○ Suggest some of the challenges such an event poses for its organisers.

● The inaccessibility of many parts of the country is a major problem, both for getting the vaccination clinics set up in mountainous regions, deserts, tropical rainforests, etc., and for the population who must make long and difficult journeys to attend them. Advertising an NID and explaining its purpose and importance is not straightforward in remote populations with high levels of illiteracy and many spoken languages. Staff must be trained to administer the vaccine correctly and safely; transport and storage facilities for supplies must be organised to ensure adequate population coverage. House-to-house follow-up has to be made to ensure that vaccinations are repeated to 'boost' immunity to protective levels.

Organisational problems such as these mean that the conduct of mass vaccination programmes is often less than ideal, particularly but not exclusively in developing countries. For example, the WHO's Immunization Safety Project (the website is given under the *Course Resources* section of the course website) reported in 1998 that up to one third of vaccinations were not being carried out in a way that guaranteed sterility, and only one third of countries importing vaccines had a monitoring system to detect vaccine-associated adverse events. The procedures for ensuring optimum storage of vaccines and disposal of injection equipment were often inadequate, and the most up-to-date vaccines could not always be afforded or obtained.

☐ What 'perverse effect' of vaccination could occur in a community where a poorly organised vaccination programme failed to achieve population coverage at or above the critical immunisation threshold? (If you are unsure, revise Book 6, Section 4.2.)

◖ The average age at infection of the unimmunised individuals in the population increases, because their contact rate with sources of infection is reduced by the pool of vaccinated people all around them. If the infection is one that causes more severe symptoms or permanent damage in older individuals (e.g. polio, mumps, hepatitis A virus), then a 'sub-threshold' vaccination programme will result in an increase in the proportion of adverse outcomes in those who develop the disease at a later age.

Perverse effects such as these have contributed to public anxiety about the safety of vaccination programmes.

3.7.3 Vaccine safety

Our views on the safety of vaccines have changed enormously since they were first introduced. Consider variolation, which preceded vaccination for smallpox (Section 3.1). The high fatality rate from smallpox meant that the 2–3% risk of death associated with variolation was considered acceptable in the seventeenth century. Nowadays however, the risk of adverse reactions is a primary consideration, partly because vaccination is usually performed on people who are well, so there is a requirement for very high safety standards.

The production of vaccines is subject to rigorous quality controls to ensure that every batch delivers the same potency, does not induce harmful autoimmune or inflammatory responses, and is free from harmful contaminants. Nevertheless, accidents have occurred in which pathogens survived in supposedly 'killed' whole-cell vaccines and live attenuated strains have occasionally reverted to pathogenicity (as the *Polio* Case Study illustrated). Vaccines are usually produced by growing pathogenic or attenuated strains in laboratory animals or in tissue cultures derived from their cells, and animal proteins may be added to tissue cultures as nutrients.

☐ What additional challenges does this pose for vaccine safety?

◖ Quality checks must ensure that no 'animal' viruses, immunogenic proteins or DNA from the vaccine donor or growth medium are present in the vaccine.

The new DNA vaccines, the use of viral or bacterial 'gene vectors' and the possibility that prions may contaminate vaccines, add further levels of complexity. (New challenges for vaccine quality control are reviewed in a WHO report by Dellepiane *et al.*, 2000.)

Most people tolerate the minor discomfort of an injection and the possibility of local swelling, slight fever or other minor symptoms in the short term following a vaccination, but more extreme or long-lasting side-effects are unacceptable. No medical procedure carries a zero risk and vaccinations are no exception, but in particular groups, such as people with immunodeficiencies, the risk is higher and vaccination with live attenuated strains may be inadvisable. Even when a vaccine has a good safety record, the perception of risk and concerns about adverse reactions can have a major impact on vaccine uptake.

3.7.4 Perceived risk of vaccination

An important consideration in vaccination programmes is the *perceived* risk associated with the vaccine. As the incidence of a disease falls (possibly as a result of vaccination), the risk of contracting it also falls. Of course, the risk to individuals from the vaccine remains the same – but what changes is the relative *importance* of the disease compared with the perceived importance of any adverse effects of the vaccine. There is less incentive to be vaccinated or to have a child vaccinated in a population with a low incidence of the disease, and concerns about possible side-effects of the vaccine can further reduce its uptake.

○ What consequence might falling vaccine uptake have for the incidence of a vaccine-preventable disease in a population? Explain the processes underlying the events you have described in terms of the concepts in Book 6, Section 4.1.

● As vaccination coverage falls, the proportion who are susceptible to the infection rises and the level of *herd immunity* to the pathogen declines. If a source of infection enters the population in conditions in which transmission to susceptible hosts is possible, an outbreak of the disease will occur. If the proportion of immunes in the population has fallen below the *critical immunisation threshold* (i.e. the proportion of the population who must be immunised for the infection to be eliminated), then – in the absence of a return to high vaccine coverage – the infection will become endemic in the community again.

The perception of risk is a subtle and complex phenomenon. Many studies have shown that people tend to *overestimate* the chance of suffering a rare adverse event (such as being struck by lightning) and *underestimate* 'everyday' sources of risk (such as traffic accidents), which are actually much more likely to happen. Public perception of the risks associated with vaccinations seems to follow this pattern, in that people in countries where a vaccine-preventable disease has fallen to a very low level tend to overestimate the residual risk associated with the vaccine. An additional consideration is that most vaccine recipients are babies or very young children who cannot 'consent' to the procedure. Parents may be more reluctant to have children vaccinated than a rational assessment of the risks and benefits would dictate, because they will feel responsible for any adverse outcomes of a procedure they deliberately chose to accept. Two examples of vaccination programmes illustrate these ideas.

In 1999, the new conjugate 'MenC' vaccine against Group C *Neisseria meningitidis*, one of several causes of meningitis, was introduced in the UK in the first mass vaccination programme with this vaccine in the world. An earlier subunit vaccine against Groups A and C was available, but had never been used in a routine vaccination schedule. No vaccine currently protects against Group B, which is twice as prevalent as Group C, but causes a less severe illness. Before 1999, there were about 1500 cases of Group C meningitis in the UK annually, with a 10% case fatality rate and an incidence of serious permanent disabilities in about 15% of those who survived. The septicaemia can cause such rapid and extensive tissue damage in the extremities that amputation of the hands, forearms and lower limbs may be unavoidable.

The vaccine was offered initially to young children, then to everyone of school age, and later to young adults (e.g. college students), these being the highest risk groups. The programme was strongly promoted by the government, health professionals and independent bodies such as the Meningitis Trust. Even though meningitis C is a rare condition – around 5 cases annually per 100 000 children aged under 5 years – parents saw it as such a serious disease that there was a high uptake of the new vaccine. The perceived threat from the disease was considered to be so great that almost all parents accepted government assurances that any risk associated with the new vaccine was low (as indeed turned out to be the case). Following the introduction of the MenC vaccine, the incidence of Group C meningitis fell by about 75%.

○ Estimate the annual number of lives saved by the introduction of the MenC vaccine in the UK.

● Around 110, based on the figures given above. With 150 fatalities annually, a 75% reduction in the disease incidence implies that mortality is reduced accordingly.

Contrast the lack of public anxiety about vaccine safety in the MenC programme, with the continuing controversy about vaccination against *Bordetella pertussis*, the causative agent of whooping cough. A pertussis vaccine has been available in the UK since the mid-1950s, accelerating the downward trend in disease incidence. However, in the mid-1970s, concern was expressed about possible neurological consequences of the vaccine. Uptake fell very rapidly from 81% to 30%, followed soon after by a sharp increase in the incidence of whooping cough (Figure 3.12).

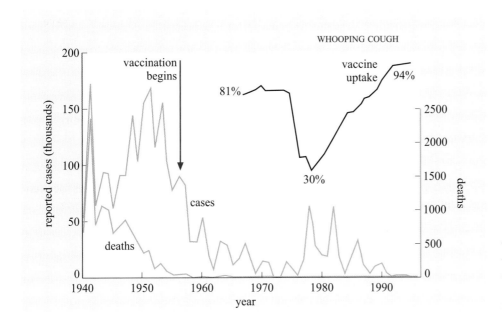

WHOOPING COUGH

FIGURE 3.12
The number of reported cases of whooping cough, and associated deaths, in England and Wales, 1940–1996, with vaccine uptake (% coverage in the target group) from 1967.

As the perceived threat of the disease rose, parental confidence in the vaccine was re-established and vaccination rates increased again, bringing the incidence of whooping cough back down to almost zero in the early 1990s.

By comparison with bacterial meningitis, whooping cough is highly contagious. The estimated value of R_0 for England and Wales in the 1970s, assuming a totally susceptible population, is 16–18 (Book 6, Table 1.1). With a transmission risk of 50–90% (i.e. effective transmission between an infective case and a susceptible individual occurs in 50–90% of contacts), most children in an unimmunised population will become infected. Thus, as vaccination rates fell in the 1970s, epidemics very quickly occurred and parents became increasingly concerned about its effects. Historically in the UK, whooping cough was a major cause of infant death, and it still carries a risk of neurological damage or detached retina due to the coughing in a minority of cases. However, as vaccination levels have risen, parental experience of the effects of whooping cough have faded, and concerns about possible adverse reactions to the vaccine have resurfaced.

The cyclical resurgence of whooping cough associated with the decline in vaccination levels highlights the societal dimension of attempts to eradicate an infectious disease. In 2002, concerns were expressed in the UK and in the USA that the combined measles, mumps and rubella vaccine (MMR) might be associated with the development of autism or gastrointestinal abnormalities. Vaccination rates have fallen in those countries, and not just in relation to MMR. Some parents have lobbied for separate vaccines against measles, mumps and rubella to replace the triple vaccine in the belief that this approach would be safer, despite government assertions that it will result in less protection. By the time you are reading this, the debate will have moved on.

Summary of Section 3.7

1   The cost of developing and testing a new vaccine is considerable; there is no incentive to develop a vaccine if there are more cost-effective or accessible ways of controlling the disease, if the population at risk cannot pay the market price, or if the disease is so rare that a vaccine would not be profitable.

2   Organisational difficulties in the delivery of mass vaccination programmes can limit their efficacy and (in certain cases) lead to perverse effects, such as an increase in the proportion of adverse outcomes if sub-threshold vaccine coverage increases the average age at infection.

3   Quality control procedures on vaccines must be rigorously applied to ensure that they deliver an effective dose and are not contaminated by potentially harmful material.

4   Perceptions of risk associated with a vaccine can lead to a decline in its uptake and subsequent resurgence of the disease. The level of concern about the safety of a vaccine tends to fluctuate in an inverse relationship with the perceived level of threat from the disease it controls. As disease incidence declines, the safety of the vaccine becomes an overriding consideration.

3.8 Internet researches into vaccination issues

Conclude your study by undertaking some broad Internet searches on key topics raised in this chapter. First, bring yourself up to date with the current status of the MMR debate. Spend about one hour on this exercise.

You will certainly find a number of sites with highly polarized opinions in the MMR debate. You should aim to evaluate the reliability of the sites you visit. What evidence do they present? Do they reference their evidence? How much use is made of quotations from individuals? What links do the websites provide? Are links to other sites selective to one side of the debate, or do they address the other side too? Here are some of the other questions that you might consider:

- Has a fall in the uptake of MMR in any country been associated with an increase in the incidence of measles, or mumps, or rubella? Is it possible to quantify the effect?

- What evidence has emerged either to support or contradict concerns about a link between MMR and autism or other adverse outcomes?

- What are the effects of measles in unvaccinated children in developing countries?

- Have concerns been expressed about possible adverse outcomes of any other vaccine, and (if so) on what evidence has this been based?

Now investigate the details of at least one other vaccination programme (in addition to the polio eradication campaign, which you should already have researched as part of the *Polio* Case Study). Spend about one hour on this exercise.

- Identify the type of vaccine used, the method of delivery and any issues that have emerged during the organisation of the programme.

- What has been the effect over time on the incidence or severity of the disease? How has this varied in different locations?

- What are the prospects for eradicating the infectious agent globally through mass vaccination programmes? What factors are delaying or threatening progress?

We have provided some links under *Course Resources* on the S320 home page to websites dedicated to vaccination data and progress reports in the UK, USA and internationally, but there are many others.

Learning outcomes for Chapter 3

When you have studied this chapter you should be able to:

3.1 Define and use, or recognize definitions and applications of, each of the terms printed in **bold** in the text. *(Question 3.1)*

3.2 Use examples from the history of vaccination to illustrate the conduct and outcomes of vaccine strategies to control infectious diseases. *(Questions 3.2 and 3.3)*

3.3 Discuss the principle strategies available for developing a vaccine and explain the significance of critical antigens, immunogens and adjuvants in developing effective vaccines. *(Questions 3.3 and 3.4)*

3.4 Identify examples of infectious diseases for which effective vaccines are available and some for which they are not. Explain why it has been scientifically difficult or commercially unprofitable to develop vaccines against certain infectious diseases, and why others have been amenable to control by vaccination. *(Questions 3.4 and 3.5)*

3.5 Discuss the prospects for developing a vaccine against a named infectious disease, given information on its biology and epidemiology, and on the immune response in human hosts. *(Question 3.5)*

3.6 Discuss limitations on the efficacy of mass vaccination programmes, and illustrate interactions between the perceived threat of an infectious disease, the perceived risk of adverse outcomes from vaccination, the level of vaccine uptake, and the consequences for public health. *(Question 3.6)*

Questions for Chapter 3

Question 3.1

Is it true to say that active vaccines are always used prophylactically, whereas passive immunisation can only be used therapeutically? Explain your answers.

Question 3.2

The following questions (several of which have quite unexpected answers) relate to your study of the article on the history of smallpox by Barquet and Domingo, which you read 'online' at the end of Section 3.1.

(a) What is the earliest evidence we have of smallpox infection?

(b) Who developed the first written theory of acquired immunity?

(c) Name four empires that were crippled by smallpox epidemics in the past.

(d) Who introduced variolation into England?

(e) What serious pathological consequence affected up to one third of the people who recovered from smallpox infection?

(f) Who was the first person to use vaccination in England?

(g) How was vaccinia virus transported from Spain to South America as part of Charles IV's programme of mass vaccination in the Spanish colonies?

Question 3.3

In what way is the vaccine against smallpox strategically different from (almost) all other active vaccines? How (in theory) might the remaining stocks of smallpox virus be useful in research to develop a new vaccine, and what criteria would a new vaccine have to fulfil?

Question 3.4

Suggest one reason why the combined diphtheria, tetanus and pertussis (DTP) vaccine has a greater efficacy against all three diseases than can be achieved by vaccinating against each infection separately.

Question 3.5

What biological and other factors have influenced the failure to develop a vaccine to control sleeping sickness in Africa (caused by trypanosoma species)?

Question 3.6

Summarise the combination of factors that are most likely to lead to a fall in the uptake of a (hypothetical) vaccine, which is only very rarely associated with an adverse outcome.

4 PUBLIC HEALTH APPROACHES TO INFECTIOUS DISEASE

This chapter aims to give a greater insight into public health approaches to controlling infectious disease, beyond those interventions based on chemicals and vaccines already discussed in this book. The diversity of activities that come under the public health banner is so great that we cannot illustrate them all, but we have chosen a wide range of examples and (wherever possible) referred to public health inputs to the 'case study' diseases highlighted in this course. Chapter 5 builds on the foundations laid here by presenting a case study of guinea worm disease (or dracunculiasis), which has been brought to the edge of global eradication entirely by public health interventions. There are no Internet exercises or CDs associated with Chapter 4.

4.1 Protecting the health of populations

We begin this chapter with a brief reminder of the global burden of infectious disease at the start of the twenty-first century, compiled from WHO, UNICEF and other international sources. This is a prelude to considering the prospects and challenges for public health approaches to controlling infection and reducing its impacts on human lives.

4.1.1 Infectious disease in the twenty-first century

In the year 2000:

*   One third of the global population (around 2 billion people) were carriers of *M. tuberculosis*, 8.8 million developed active TB and almost 2 million people with chronic TB died;

*   More than 36 million people were estimated to be living with HIV infection, over 5 million new infections occurred and 3 million people died;

*   Over 350 million people were chronically infected with hepatitis B virus (HBV) and 170 million with hepatitis C virus (HCV), causing over 1 million deaths from liver disease and hepatic cancer;

*   Excluding HIV and HBV, there were around 350 million new cases of the major sexually-transmitted infections, including syphilis and gonorrhoea;

*   More than 300 million new cases of malaria occurred and around 1 million people died, most of them children aged under 5 years;

*   4 million people died from acute respiratory infections – more than half of them children;

*   2.2 million died from diarrhoeal diseases, nearly all of them children; 875 000 children died from measles, 377 000 from tetanus and 295 000 from whooping cough; bacterial meningitis killed a further 171 000;

*   Dengue viruses caused an estimated 50–100 million episodes of illness, including at least 250 000 cases of haemorrhagic fever and 24 000 deaths;

- Around 1.5 billion people were infected with intestinal worms; a typical child in a poor environment in a developing country commonly carries around 1000 hookworms, roundworms and whipworms, causing anaemia, stunted growth and increased vulnerability to other diseases;

- The 'tropical' diseases killed 171 000 people, but their impact on human lives can best be judged by their population prevalence: leishmaniasis (2 million cases annually), schistosomiasis (1.2 million symptomatic cases), Chagas' disease (1 million), sleeping sickness (500 000) and yellow fever (200 000).

The burden of disability, sickness and death associated with infectious diseases is overwhelmingly suffered by people in developing countries, where children are disproportionately at risk. Their situation would undoubtedly be very much worse without the chemical interventions and vaccination programmes discussed in Chapters 2 and 3. But at the start of the twenty-first century, there were no *curative* chemical agents for any viral diseases and no effective vaccines against some of the most important infections, including HIV, malaria, the dengue viruses and most of the agents causing sexually-transmitted, tropical and diarrhoeal diseases. Drug-resistance was increasing in the agents of many infectious diseases, including TB, malaria and sleeping sickness, and insecticide-resistance was growing in several vector species.

Perhaps most important of all, 1.1 billion people (more than one sixth of the world's population) had no access to clean water (Figure 4.1) and 2.4 billion (40% of global population) did not have adequate sanitation.

FIGURE 4.1
Children collect items that may have some value from the rubbish floating in Manila Bay in the Philippines. More than one sixth of the world's population have no access to safe water for drinking or washing and 2.4 billion people lack adequate sanitation.

In this chapter we illustrate the diversity of public health approaches to controlling the huge burden of infectious diseases, focusing on methods *other* than medical treatments and vaccines. An additional aim is to demonstrate the importance of addressing local needs and engaging local communities in interventions to improve public health.

4.1.2 The scope of public health

In Chapter 1, we distinguished three overlapping uses of the term 'public health', which we can now elaborate. Public health encompasses:

- the health of the population as a whole, as estimated by many different indicators;

- the strategies and interventions aimed at improving an aspect of health, or reducing the incidence or impact of disease, throughout the population at risk;

- the multi-professional discipline whose members devise and deliver those strategies and interventions, monitor the outcomes in the population, and review procedures that may lead to further improvements.

A classic definition of public health dates from 1920:

> Public health is the science and art of preventing disease, prolonging life, and promoting health and efficiency through organized community effort for the sanitation of the environment. The control of community infections, the education of the individual, principles of personal hygiene, the organization of medical and nursery services for the early diagnosis and preventive treatment of disease, and the development of the social machinery which will ensure to every individual of the community a standard of living adequate for the maintenance of health.
>
> (Winslow, 1920, p. 183)

It is as well to remember that in 1920 the treatment of infectious diseases was in its infancy. Only one group of antimicrobial agents (the arsenicals) had been identified for use in syphilis, and these compounds, together with some synthetic dyes, were also used to treat some protoctist infections (look back at Box 2.2). There were very few vaccines available (as Table 3.1 showed), though passive immunisation against tetanus had saved thousands of lives among soldiers in World War I, and the diphtheria antitoxin had cut the death rate among children. So, although the organisation of 'medical and nursery services' was seen as important in the 1920s, the best hope of 'preventing disease, prolonging life and promoting health and efficiency' was to improve sanitation, personal hygiene and living standards for all – the same strategies advocated by the sanitarian movement a century earlier. And they remain central to achieving the development goals adopted by the United Nations at its Millennium Summit in 2000 (Box 4.1).

BOX 4.1	United Nations Millennium Declaration

Resolved, by the year 2015: to halve the proportion of the world's people whose income is less than one dollar a day and the proportion of people who suffer from hunger; to halve the proportion of people who are unable to reach or to afford safe drinking water; to ensure that children everywhere, boys and girls alike, will be able to complete a full course of primary schooling and that girls and boys will have equal access to all levels of education; to reduce maternal mortality by three quarters, and under-five child mortality by two thirds, of their current rates; to have halted and begun to reverse the spread of HIV/AIDS, the scourge of malaria and other major diseases that afflict humanity; to provide special assistance to children orphaned by HIV/AIDS.

Resolved, by 2020: to have achieved a significant improvement in the lives of at least 100 million slum dwellers.

(UN, 2000; summary of the resolution on development and poverty eradication, paragraph 19)

Notice that the UN's goals cannot be disentangled into those that relate to infectious disease and those that do not. People who live on less than one dollar a day cannot afford safe drinking water; 100 million inhabitants of urban slums and shanty towns cannot protect themselves from sources of infection; children who are frequently ill cannot complete their schooling. The outlook is not without hope: the advances in infrastructure, communication and organisation at local, national and international levels that delivered such large improvements in public health in the 'developed' world in the twentieth century are being applied in developing countries with substantial success.

But the prospects for meeting the UN's targets (Box 4.1) are constrained by many factors: how little can be afforded in heavily indebted countries (as Table 4.1 later in this chapter illustrates); the shortage of skills, scientific knowledge and facilities; difficult circumstances of geology and climate; the level of illiteracy and gender inequality; and the extent to which political will, social stability and community action can be harnessed for the public good.

4.1.3 Professional support and community action

Raising the standards of public health is not simply a matter of training more doctors and nurses, building more hospitals and providing more funding for vaccines and treatments – though all of these make substantial contributions. As the examples in this chapter demonstrate, most of the work involved in delivering public health strategies occurs *outside* the formal health care system, and (as Winslow's 1920 definition states) 'organized community effort' is still an essential element. Consider this fictional example of a potential public health crisis in an advanced industrial economy. Following a coded warning from a terrorist group, an open container of white powder is found in a busy London street. The presence of *Bacillus anthracis* is confirmed.

○ What professional groups would be involved in attempts to protect public health in this situation?

● You would need: microbiologists to test potential contacts for infection; scientists and technicians to prepare additional stocks of anthrax vaccine; environmental health officers, infection-control specialists and local authority personnel to set up vaccination clinics, organise the distribution of anthrax vaccine, decide on who is to be vaccinated and why, and maintain accurate records; the police or army to place a cordon around the contaminated area, assist in maintaining quarantine restrictions and to help trace people who may have been infected; specialist hospital staff to treat cases of anthrax; social workers and counsellors to deal with local panic and distress; media specialists and politicians to conduct a campaign of public reassurance to stop the 'worried well' from swamping the health system (as occurred in the early stages of the HIV epidemic in the UK).

Thus, the protection of public health involves many groups of professionals with different skills and expertise, employing a wide range of technologies. But their efforts would be thwarted without the active participation of the individuals in the communities they serve.

○ Explain why community participation is central to the success of public health strategies in an emergency such as the one outlined above.

● The risks to the population can only be brought under control if members of the affected community support the measures introduced for their protection, e.g. in accepting restrictions on freedom of movement, or coming forward for vaccination, or heeding public information advice about when medical help should or should not be sought.

The responses described in this fictional example are similar to those that operate in genuine outbreaks of potentially fatal infectious disease in locations with modern public health infrastructures and trained personnel. An **outbreak** refers to two or more cases of an infectious disease linked by clinical, epidemiological or microbiological evidence. For example, in 2003 the first acknowledged outbreak of severe acute respiratory syndrome (SARS) was identified initially from clinical evidence of people with symptoms of an unusually acute pneumonia that caused death in 5–10% of cases. It was subsequently tracked epidemiologically, from the first publicly identified case in Hong Kong, back to its origins in Southern China, and from contacts of 'patient zero' who flew to Toronto in Canada and Hanoi in Viet Nam, where local outbreaks developed. The link between affected individuals was subsequently confirmed microbiologically when they were found to have been infected by a previously unknown corona virus.

In examples such as these, public health officials take the lead in identifying individuals who are or who may have been infected, and in supervising arrangements for treatment and disease prevention, including quarantine in extreme cases. The infectious agent and its source is identified and (ideally) eliminated; procedures that could have prevented the outbreak are reviewed and if possible improved; and strategies for reducing the impact of any future outbreak are considered and implemented.

However, in remote or poor parts of the world, the local infrastructure and organisation is often inadequate to bring sudden outbreaks of life-threatening infections quickly under control. For example, consider what is required to resolve an epidemic of cholera in a refugee camp in Afghanistan, or to prevent one case of Ebola fever in a Congolese village from spreading to hundreds of neighbouring people. Even well-funded public health systems can struggle to cope, as the outbreaks of SARS in Hong Kong and Toronto demonstrated.

But such high-profile epidemics are only the tip of the public health 'iceberg'. Submerged below the level that excites media interest are the day-to-day public health routines of surveillance, intervention, education and community action that seek to control infection all over the world. Although these strategies save millions of lives every year and prevent many more episodes of infectious disease, they are largely disregarded outside public health circles. In the rest of this chapter, we aim to give you an insight into their diversity, their impact and the constraints on their success.

Summary of Section 4.1

1   The global burden of infectious disease remains a significant threat to health, economic development and equity of opportunity, particularly in developing countries and disproportionately among children.

2   In addition to chemical strategies (Chapter 2) and vaccination programmes (Chapter 3), public health approaches to infection control have traditionally

focused on the provision of safe water and sanitation, the promotion of hygiene, and the organisation of surveillance and response strategies in disease outbreaks. Raising living standards and improving the quality of housing, nutrition and education are also integral to the public health approach.

3 The protection and promotion of public health relies on community action in collaboration with professional support.

4.2 Levels of prevention

In this section we examine a hierarchy of public health interventions, which are traditionally considered to operate at different 'levels of prevention'. Although you should be aware that there is some artificiality in separating them in this way, it provides a useful framework to illustrate the diversity of public health strategies.

4.2.1 Primary prevention strategies

Public health strategies aimed at the **primary prevention** of infectious disease seek to prevent new cases of infection from occurring. Vaccination is the most obvious example, but there are many others – for example, the free distribution of condoms in areas of high HIV prevalence, coupled with 'safe sex' education and other interventions to promote behavioural changes that reduce exposure to sexually-transmitted infections (STIs). Food safety legislation and inspection of catering premises and slaughterhouses are further examples of primary prevention. Food handling practices by the individual are also important: food that is properly washed, cooked or stored is less likely to be contaminated with the organisms that cause outbreaks of food poisoning (a subject we return to in Section 4.5). As you will see as this chapter progresses, many of the examples of public health interventions we discuss are operating at the primary level.

4.2.2 Secondary prevention

Secondary prevention aims to detect new cases of infectious disease at the earliest possible stage and intervene in ways that prevent or reduce the risk of infection from spreading further in the population. This level of prevention involves infected (or exposed) individuals in seeking early treatment or participating in screening programmes. Benefit to the individual is dependent on the availability of treatment, but the primary aim from a public health perspective is to protect the community rather than to aid personal recovery. It requires the provision of community infrastructures and organisations to educate the population about signs of illness that require prompt treatment, coupled with surveillance or screening to detect cases quickly and to determine the need for treatment services and preventive actions.

Surveillance is the collection of data on the occurrence of the infection in the community and it forms the essential basis for targeting public health interventions. An example might be the collection of anonymous prevalence data on certain pathogens in antenatal blood samples, or from people attending clinics specializing in the treatment of STIs. Surveillance systems are not concerned directly with treatment and those that collect data anonymously cannot identify 'cases' as individuals. In Chapter 5, you will learn more about the surveillance system that mapped the global occurrence of guinea worm disease, village by village throughout the endemic areas, to determine the best methods of intervention in relation to local needs.

Individuals can also be systematically tested for infection in **screening programmes**. The service can be targeted on groups assumed to be at high risk; for example, in the UK, 'rough sleepers' and people staying in migrant hostels are at greatest risk of TB. Mass screening programmes aim to reach the whole population, as in the national campaigns of the 1940s and 50s to detect signs of pulmonary tuberculosis in chest X-rays. Clinical and/or microbiological screening programmes are a vital component of public health initiatives against infectious diseases all over the world, with the aim of secondary prevention as well the treatment of individuals (Figure 4.2).

FIGURE 4.2
Villagers in Ethiopia at a local health clinic give blood smears for the malaria screening programme. Screening helps to protect others in the community: early treatment of uncomplicated malaria prevents parasites from developing to the stage where mosquitoes can ingest them with a blood meal and transmit the infection to new hosts.

Secondary prevention of infectious disease has most to contribute to public health where the condition is both treatable and chronic, particularly if it has an asymptomatic stage or can exist in a carrier state (described in Chapter 3).

☐ Suggest some examples (other than TB and malaria) that fit these criteria.

◖ Other persistent infections in which the individual remains a significant risk to others unless treatment is obtained include viral hepatitis, typhoid, schistosomiasis, lymphatic filariasis, syphilis and gonorrhoea.

Even if the condition is not curable by medical treatment, benefit to the community may also result if screening and counselling of infected people leads to behaviour modification; for example, the rates of new HIV infection among gay men in the UK declined in the late 1980s due to voluntary changes in sexual behaviour.

4.2.3 Tertiary prevention

Medical treatment to prevent the worst outcomes of a disease in an individual is known as **tertiary prevention**. Although this may greatly improve the quality of life for that person, it has at most a limited impact on the spread of infectious disease. For example, physical therapies that support the rehabilitation of children with paralytic polio are at the tertiary level of prevention, i.e. they can reduce the impact of paralysis on the child's quality of life – but they have no impact whatever on the spread of polio virus in a community. However, tertiary level interventions

FIGURE 4.3 Tertiary prevention can benefit the community as well as the individual. This man with elephantiasis in both legs, due to lymphatic infection with filarial worms, follows a rigorous hygiene regime daily, washing with soap and water and applying antibiotic cream, which has enabled him to work at a local coir factory in India.

contribute to public health in a more subtle way. By alleviating the pain, distress and disability experienced by individuals, the community as a whole benefits from the input these people are enabled to make to the 'social capital' of all (Figure 4.3).

To see how the hierarchy of prevention levels can operate in practice, consider the *Tuberculosis* Case Study.

☐ What measures can be taken against TB at the primary, secondary and tertiary levels of prevention?

⬛ Primary prevention: BCG vaccination and improved living standards, including better housing (reduction in crowding) and nutrition (improved host immunity).

Secondary prevention: screening programmes to detect cases of infection early (e.g. from sputum tests); treatment of early non-symptomatic infection with drugs such as isoniazid, or symptomatic TB with a multi-drug regimen, ideally in a DOTs programme (directly observed treatment).

Tertiary prevention: drug treatment of severe complications such as tubercular meningitis, and physical rehabilitation therapy for tuberculosis affecting bones and mobility.

The same principles can be applied to unfamiliar examples.

☐ Identify the level of prevention operating in each of the following strategies to control diarrhoeal diseases in children in a rural village in a low-income country:

(i)   Drilling a deep tube-well to access clean water and pumping it to stand-pipes.

(ii) Digging cesspits and building latrines.

(iii) Vaccinating children against typhoid.

(iv) Teaching parents how to make and administer oral rehydration salts (ORS).

(v)   Educating parents and children about the importance of hand-washing before preparing food and after going to the toilet.

(vi) Administering intravenous fluids to children suffering severe dehydration due to persistent diarrhoea.

⬛ Strategies (i)–(iii) and (v) are examples of primary prevention to reduce the number of new cases of diarrhoea; (iv) is secondary prevention because ORS shortens the duration of the illness and thus reduces the spread of causative organisms; (vi) is tertiary prevention, aimed at saving lives.

In Section 4.4.4, we return to this example to consider how cultural context and respect for human dignity can influence the success of public health strategies.

Summary of Section 4.2

Three levels of prevention of infectious diseases can be identified in a public health context. Primary prevention aims to prevent new cases from occurring; secondary prevention aims to treat the disease at the earliest stage to prevent it from spreading; and tertiary prevention aims to alleviate the worst effects of an established disease in an individual, which may indirectly benefit the community.

4.3 Levels of intervention

The examples of disease prevention discussed in the previous section are, in the main, focused on individuals, or they operate within the local community. However, many public health programmes are coordinated regionally or nationally, and still others have an international dimension. This gives us another 'hierarchy' of levels to illustrate the diversity of public health approaches to controlling infectious disease.

4.3.1 Strategies focused on individuals

As you have already seen, many public health interventions operate at the level of the individual, even though the intention or the effect is to reduce the risk of infection in the community as a whole.

☐ Explain how the promotion of breast feeding can benefit public health as well as breast-fed babies.

▣ Breast feeding is promoted not only for its nutritional benefits, but to protect breast-fed infants against the pathogens that can contaminate feeding bottles, animal milk and infant formula prepared with unsafe water. Breast milk also contains maternal antibodies, so it provides babies with passive immunity against enteric pathogens. If more mothers breast feed, there will be fewer babies with diarrhoea to infect others in the community.

In the context of infectious diesease, public health strategies focused on individuals can be distinguished into those involving medical treatment or case containment, isolation of the infected individual, vaccination and the promotion of personal hygiene.

Medical treatment and case containment

Curative treatments obviously reduce the number of sources of infection in the community, but treatments that only reduce the extent or duration of symptoms may also have some impact on the spread of disease: for example, the spread of a respiratory infection may be reduced if coughing and sneezing by infected people is reduced by medication. Similarly, transmission may be reduced by **case containment**, i.e. treatment that 'contains' a source of infection so that it is less likely to be passed on to others. In Chapter 5, we refer to case containment to reduce the transmission of guinea worms by bandaging the site of parasite emergence.

☐ At which level of prevention is this strategy operating?

▣ Case containment is an example of secondary prevention.

However, as noted in Section 4.2.3, non-curative treatments generally have at most only a marginal impact on the transmission of infection. For example, HAART drug regimens (Chapter 2) can delay the development of AIDS in people with HIV infection, but they cannot prevent transmission of the virus or halt the HIV epidemic. On the contrary, it is possible that by increasing the lifespan of people with HIV and by creating a false sense of security in the uninfected population, the availability of these drugs could increase the rate at which HIV spreads in some populations.

Quarantine and voluntary isolation

Quarantine is one of the oldest forms of public health intervention, pre-dating the germ theory of disease. All societies have enforced the isolation of infected individuals at some time to prevent an infectious agent from spreading in a community, as in the notorious case of the cook known as 'typhoid Mary' who was imprisoned in the USA from 1907–1910 and again in 1915 (this time for 23 years) when she refused to give up her profession. Nowadays, public health inspectors can enforce the exclusion of catering workers from food handling if they are infected with a causative agent of food poisoning, and they usually have to demonstrate freedom from infection in three consecutive stool samples before they can return to work.

Voluntary quarantine at home has also been important in containing certain outbreaks: for example, people who were in contact with SARS cases were supposed to stay in isolation at home for at least ten days. However, the isolation of suspected or confirmed cases of highly infectious diseases has generally occurred in hospitals.

○ What dilemma does this strategy pose?

● Hospitals have the best facilities for treating the infected individual, while ensuring that 'barrier methods' of care reduce significant contacts with other people. But hospitals are also communities of the unwell who are likely to be more susceptible to infection than the population at large. Even if staff who are caring for quarantined patients are scrupulous in observing strict infection-control procedures, the infectious agent may spread to health professionals and then to other patients (as occurred in the 2003 SARS epidemic).

In the nineteenth and early twentieth centuries, 'fever' hospitals and TB sanitaria were built outside major centres of population in Europe and the USA, to quarantine their patients away from the rest of society. In 2003, an isolation hospital was constructed in Southern China to quarantine people infected with the SARS virus.

Vaccination revisited

Although parents tend to think of vaccination as protecting their children as individuals (and of course this is true), the extent of vaccine coverage in the community is vital to the protective effect.

○ Vaccination of the individual protects the community in two ways (Book 6, Chapter 4; and Chapter 3 of this book). What are they?

● (i) The increase in herd immunity reduces the frequency of person-to-person transmission, so the ability of the infectious agent to spread is reduced. (ii) The amount of infective agent circulating will also usually be reduced.

These effects are well illustrated by consideration of rubella vaccination (the R in MMR). The most serious outcomes of rubella infection are foetal abnormalities, which can occur when a non-immune woman becomes infected with the virus during early pregnancy. Thus, one might assume that routine rubella vaccination was only a priority for girls. However, unless a high proportion of boys are also vaccinated, so that the critical immunisation threshold in the population as a whole is exceeded (Book 6 identified the threshold for rubella as 75–85%), the virus will continue to circulate in the population, and unvaccinated girls who do not contract rubella before pregnancy remain at risk of infection.

○ Why have the most successful global public health interventions to date (the eradication of smallpox and the near elimination of polio) relied on vaccination?

● In principle, vaccine delivery is a simple event, which involves no changes to social structures or long-term personal behaviour and is relatively cheap to organise and deliver. Thus, the success of the programme is not dependent on radical changes in society.

Other public health interventions, such as the provision of water and sanitation, involve huge expense and a significant degree of social adaptation. Prevention that relies on changes in personal behaviour may be difficult to sustain.

FIGURE 4.4
Women and children from a sugar plantation in Ethiopia gather around the only local water collection point to fill containers for drinking, washing and cooking at home. The need to carry water from distant stand-pipes influences the level of personal hygiene that can be maintained.

Personal hygiene

When clean water and sanitation were installed in London in the nineteenth century, the epidemics of cholera that had claimed thousands of lives rapidly came under control. But typhoid fever continued to be a problem for several more decades. The eventual reduction in typhoid was ascribed to the increasing availability of piped water and soap inside domestic households, the safe disposal of waste water from houses, and the increasing social imperative for personal hygiene. Another infection that can be controlled by personal hygiene is typhus, because frequent washing of the body and clothing reduces the frequency of its vector, the human body louse. Note that although personal hygiene is a matter for the individual, it also requires the provision of certain infrastructures (Figure 4.4), the means to purchase certain goods (e.g. soap, domestic cleaning agents) and a culture that is supportive of cleanliness.

In public health parlance, **hygiene behaviour** encompasses the wide range of actions taken by individuals to maintain a standard of cleanliness of their bodies, domestic environments and workplaces that prevents the transmission of infection. For example, hygiene behaviour includes all the personal actions associated with excretion and the disposal of human waste and refuse, the washing of persons, clothing, implements and structures (e.g. floors, lavatories), the handling of domestic animals, and the preparation of food. The importance of the most obvious hygiene behaviour – thorough hand-washing with soap – cannot be underestimated. Although many intestinal infections are thought of as water-borne and can indeed be transmitted by that route, the agents of typhoid (from carriers) and diarrhoeal diseases (from cases) can be controlled by thorough hand-washing in an environment with adequate sanitary provision. For example, a meta-analysis (a systematic review of all research studies published on a particular topic) found that:

> … interventions to promote washing hands with soap were associated with a decreased risk of diarrhoeal disease of 47% (confidence interval 24–63%). Handwashing was also associated with a 48–59% reduced risk of more severe outcomes…estimates of the number of lives that could be saved by the universal adoption of handwashing with soap [average at] about 1.07 million [per year].

(Curtis and Cairncross, 2003, pp. 278–279)

117

We have already discussed the importance of hand-washing in health care settings to prevent cross-infection between patients and the spread of hospital acquired infections (Book 1, Chapter 1; see also Chapter 2 of this book). In Section 4.5, we discuss hand-washing further in the context of food-borne pathogens spread by inadequate safety procedures in the catering industry.

4.3.2 Community, regional and national campaigns

Many public health interventions operate at the level of the community, the region or the country as a whole; for example, the chlorination of drinking water is one of the most successful strategies in preventing infectious disease. Here we consider the provision and maintenance of the infrastructures necessary to promote public health, the enforcement of legislation and standards, the training of public health professionals and community health workers, and specific infection-control campaigns.

Infrastructure

We have already referred to the **infrastructure** of a society several times in this chapter without giving a formal definition. The term encompasses the physical structures and facilities essential to the activities of a society and its economic basis. The infrastructures most closely associated with public health and the control of infection are water supplies and sewerage (often abbreviated to WSS in public health literature). It is of historical interest that London's sewers were installed, at least in part, for aesthetic reasons to control the 'Great Stink'. The public health significance of clean water was not accepted until later, perhaps as a consequence of the investigation of the 1892 Hamburg cholera outbreak.

○ Mains sewers are advocated as the best way of disposing of faeces. So why aren't they installed everywhere?

● You might have thought about:
- Cost: Even rich countries cannot afford a full sewerage system in every centre of habitation; for example the process has not been completed in Japan or the USA; in most parts of Greece the sewerage system cannot cope with toilet paper. The cost of installing enclosed sewers in poor countries would be astronomical, even if it was technically feasible.
- Geology: Many areas of human habitation could not support a sewerage system; some settlements are built in mountains or deserts, on seashores or above the permafrost line, where underground sewers could not be constructed.
- Water supply: Sewers need a lot of water to move the waste to a site of treatment or disposal. This is not always available. An oil-rich desert country may afford to distil sea water to drink, but not for flushing sewers!
- Flooding: Too much water is as bad as too little. In recent floods in the UK many sewers overflowed. In countries with a high water-table, e.g. Bangladesh and Thailand, flooding would be constant. Built-up latrines, above ground level, are more practical and affordable.

Thus, the potential for public health to 'triumph' over some major infectious diseases through the installation of sewers is dependent on a geographical environment in which such projects are possible and the availability of adequate finance. Infrastructural interventions are 'site specific' as well as subject to economic constraints.

○ In addition to sewerage, and excluding the hospitals and health clinics, what other civic infrastructures can you think of that are involved in maintaining public health in relation to infectious disease?

● Among many other examples, you may have thought of facilities that collect and dispose of household waste – rubbish tips attract rats, flies and other vectors of disease. Slaughterhouses, meat processing plants and all the other industrial and commercial premises involved in food production, packaging, transport and sale have an important role in infection control. Air conditioning systems and water storage tanks must also be properly maintained; lapses have led to fatal outbreaks of legionnaire's disease. And the infrastructure of the education system is vital to support an informed, health-promoting community.

Legislation and standards

In Victorian England it was the various Public Health Acts that made possible the infrastructural developments needed to improve the health of the population. Many legally enforced quality standards and industry guidelines have since been developed in the UK in an attempt to ensure that the materials and services available to the public are of a sufficient standard to maintain public health. For example, microbiological standards exist for the quality of drinking water, and there are non-statutory guidelines on the microbial content of ready-to-eat foods sampled at the point of sale. Not surprisingly, there is immense variation in the legislation and standards relating to the protection of public health from infectious diseases around the world. We can do no more than draw your attention to their importance and to the difficulties that all countries encounter in enforcing them.

Training and accreditation

The delivery of public health is a complex matter and requires the skills of many different professionals. The training and accreditation of public health doctors, microbiologists, environmental health officers, occupational health specialists, meat inspectors, sanitation engineers, and so forth, generally has to be undertaken at the national level. However, the success of public health strategies all over the world, but especially in developing countries and more particularly in rural areas and in slum or shanty settlements, relies crucially on the activities of **community health workers** (or CHWs) with minimal training to meet local needs.

Since the 1960s and 70s, many developing countries have been directing more resources to primary health care teams in local communities. Although the work may be organised by professionally trained health workers, many of the interventions that protect and promote public health are entirely reliant on CHWs. The extent of their training and the equipment they are provided with are highly variable from place to place, and so too is whether they are paid or work voluntarily. Some offer a range of screening and treatment services, while others are engaged only in tackling a specific disease. The malaria screening clinic shown in Figure 4.2 is run by a CHW with basic training and rudimentary equipment; later in this chapter we refer to other examples (e.g. Figure 4.7).

Infection-control campaigns

Every country in the world is faced with particular threats from certain infectious diseases, and regional and national campaigns are organised to attempt to bring them under control; for example, the national immunisation days (NIDs) to tackle polio in countries such as India and Nigeria (*Polio* Case Study). Figure 4.5 illustrates another example, and in Section 4.4, we discuss condom distribution schemes to control the spread of HIV in South Africa, and the promotion of insecticide-treated mosquito nets for malaria control in endemic regions in Tanzania and Viet Nam.

FIGURE 4.5
A tsetse fly 'catching trap' hangs near the only source of water for a village in Cameroon, West Africa, as part of a programme to prevent sleeping sickness. The flies are attracted to the colour blue but won't land on it, so four black cloth tunnels lead to the transparent net cage at the top of the trap, which catches the flies as they move towards the light.
(Photo courtesy of Ken Hudson)

It is worth emphasizing that regional and national infection-control campaigns are not confined to the developing world: consider the legislation and slaughterhouse inspection regimes introduced in the UK in response to the link between bovine spongiform encephalopathy (BSE) in the national cattle herd, and the identification of variant Creutzfeldt-Jakob disease (vCJD) in humans; or the government publicity campaigns concerning the safety of the MMR vaccine after parents became concerned about a possible link with autism.

☐ Which emerging infectious diseases (EIDs) have been the subject of public health campaigns in the USA in recent years?

◼ You may have thought of the efforts to control HIV (which had killed almost half a million Americans by 2002; recall the *HIV* Case Study in Book 3); or to protect people from Lyme disease in forested regions (Book 2, Section 2.7.2); or to halt the spread of West Nile fever across America from the initial outbreak in New York in 1999 (the virus was possibly imported by exotic birds acquired by the city zoo; Book 1, Chapter 1).

☐ Which vector-borne disease has the highest incidence in Argentina, Brazil, Bolivia and Paraguay, and how would you expect it to be tackled?

◼ South America reports over one million people affected by Chagas' disease annually. Systematic efforts have been made to control it by spraying homes and outbuildings with insecticide to kill the reduviid bugs that spread *Trypanosoma cruzi* (recall the life cycle in Book 2, Figures 5.4 and 5.5).

The importance of community participation in the success of national campaigns is illustrated by the effect of oral rehydration salts (ORS) on childhood deaths from diarrhoeal diseases (the composition of ORS was given in Chapter 2). Since its introduction in 1979, more than 80 developing countries have established national 'Control of Diarrhoeal Diseases' campaigns promoting the use of pre-prepared ORS sachets (over 800 million are distributed free every year), or home-made rehydration solutions for children with diarrhoea. The increasing uptake of oral rehydration therapy can be seen in Figure 4.6. Although the contribution of ORS to the decline in diarrhoeal deaths among children from 4.6 million in 1980 to around 2 million in 2000 cannot be quantified accurately, a WHO review placed 'special emphasis' on its importance (Victoria *et al.*, 2000).

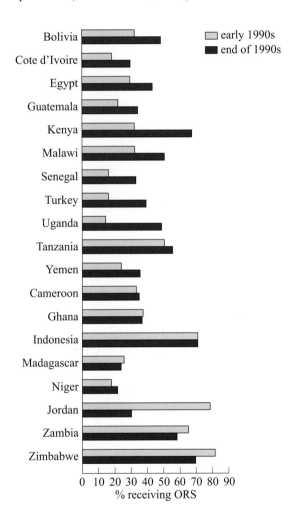

FIGURE 4.6
Change during the 1990s in the percentage of children with diarrhoea who received oral rehydration therapy prepared from ORS sachets or home-made solutions, in selected countries.

◯ What evidence does Figure 4.6 supply for the claim that national campaigns influence the uptake of oral rehydration therapy in children with diarrhoea?

⬤ The change in uptake is highly variable between countries, including those in similar geographic regions (for example, compare the trends in Kenya and Uganda with those in Ghana and Niger; or compare Egypt with Jordan). This suggests that uptake of ORS is dependent on the strength of national efforts to promote it.

Thus, the participation of local communities in public health campaigns and the quality of the surveillance, screening, treatment and prevention services they can harness is crucial to their success or failure. In Section 4.4, we examine some of the factors that can tip the balance in either direction.

4.3.3 The international level

Travel and trade

The rise of the foreign holiday and the mass population migrations triggered by conflict and economic hardship are characteristics of the modern world. It is not that people did not travel in the past, but now the opportunities and the needs are much greater. The advent of cheap air travel presents a whole new challenge to public health systems, which must now combat new infections that can spread globally in a short time. Similarly, trade routes still transport infected goods within countries as they have always done, but air freight enables infectious agents in foodstuffs to travel between continents in less than a day. Globalization needs global solutions, and although these are a long way off, many aspects of trade and travel are governed by international agreements, some of which have the potential to affect the human rights of the individual.

○ Suggest some examples that have human rights implications.

● You may have considered border health checks and whether people who appear ill should be excluded or placed in compulsory quarantine. Some countries require travellers to carry international vaccination certificates before they can enter, but should individuals who oppose vaccination be prevented from travelling?

Global public health organisations

Finally, we must mention the immense contribution to public health and the control of infectious disease by international organisations such as the WHO, UNICEF and charities such as Oxfam, Water Aid and countless other non-governmental and voluntary organisations that work all over the world.

In the next section we turn to some of the issues that influence the success of public health interventions, using a number of specific examples to illustrate more general themes.

Summary of Section 4.3

1   Public health interventions may be focused on the individual (e.g. vaccination, quarantine, improving personal hygiene), or on the community (e.g. surveillance and screening programmes).

2   Interventions to improve public health infrastructures, legislation and training are organised at community, regional or national levels; international trade and travel agreements and the work of international organisations (e.g. WHO) contribute at a global level to public health approaches to infectious disease.

3   Community participation and community health workers with minimal training and equipment are central to the success of specific infection-control campaigns in many parts of the world.

4.4 Public health priorities and the future

In this section, we consider a number of issues that face the public health movement in the twenty-first century. They range from questions about the ideology that drives modern public health policy-making at the highest level, to concerns about affordability and sustainability of specific initiatives, debates about who pays the bills, and the importance of understanding the cultural context of public health programmes. This selection in no way encompasses the breadth of considerations about public health priorities and the future – but it should offer some illustrations and insights.

4.4.1 The 'new public health': dream or reality?

In 1958, the WHO adopted an ambitious definition of **positive health** as a state of complete physical, psychological and social wellbeing. Thus, health was identified as a positive attribute and not simply the absence of disease or infirmity. Although the WHO's aspiration of 'Health for All by the Year 2000' proved to be wildly optimistic, it lay behind declarations emerging from a succession of WHO conferences in the 1970s and 1980s, which advocated (among other things) a route map for what became known as the **new public health** (Box 4.2).

The Victorian founders of the 'old public health' emphasized threats arising from the *physical* environment and they sought sanitarian solutions such as building sewers. In the 1990s, this emphasis remained, but the 'new public health' remit was extended to include the *socio-economic* environment and tackling the ways in which it contributed to inequalities in health within societies and between countries.

At the most general level, the link between wealth and health can be illustrated by Table 4.1 overleaf, which relates total per capita expenditure on health to the average expectation of years of *healthy* life for babies born in 2000 in eight of the 191 member states reporting to the WHO. In this case, we have arbitrarily chosen all the countries beginning with 'U' in the *World Health Report 2002*. The aspiration of positive health has led to greater emphasis being placed on **healthy life expectancy** – the proportion of the lifespan spent free from illness or disability – than on life expectancy as a whole.

BOX 4.2   'The new public health'

1 The emphasis on treating and curing illness should give way to a new emphasis on disease prevention and the promotion of positive health, with government support through the development of health-promoting public policies;

2 The emphasis on hospital-based care should be redirected towards primary health care services in the community;

3 The health sector as the sole provider of services should be replaced by multi-sectoral action, involving public/private partnerships (e.g. between businesses, social services, environmental departments, charities, voluntary organizations and international agencies);

4 Professional dominance of public health decision-making should be replaced by community participation in and ownership of these processes, supported by action to develop the necessary skills at community level through health education and training.

TABLE 4.1 Per capita total spending on health* for selected countries, 1995–2000, with estimated healthy life expectancy (HALE) for babies born in 2000.

Country	1995 (US$)	1996 (US$)	1997 (US$)	1998 (US$)	1999 (US$)	2000 (US$)	HALE (years)
Uganda	11	10	11	11	11	10	37.5
Ukraine	42	43	54	42	27	26	57.5
United Arab Emirates	619	631	729	752	758	767	62.4
UK	1357	1422	1531	1657	1753	1747	69.2
United Republic of Tanzania	7	9	10	10	11	12	37.8
USA	3621	3762	3905	4068	4252	4499	67.4
Uruguay	552	606	662	697	682	653	64.7
Uzbekistan	21	28	26	24	27	30	53.4

* Health spending estimates are in 'US dollars' at the prevailing exchange rate and include all sources of health expenditure from government and non-governmental organisations, health insurance schemes, private payments to practitioners and spending on over-the-counter medication and appliances. (Data from the Statistical Annex to the WHO *Annual Report 2002*, which can be accessed by following the link under *Course Resources* on the course website.)

The relationship between healthy life expectancy and health expenditure is immediately apparent from Table 4.1 in the differences between those countries spending more than US$650 per capita on health, and the rest. It is also noticeable that much higher spending may not result in a commensurate health gain (e.g. compare the UK with the USA). You may have been surprised that the Eastern European states of Ukraine and Uzbekistan can afford to spend little more on health than Uganda and the United Republic of Tanzania. The break-up of the former Soviet Union has had a profound effect on the provision of health services in the region, as Table 4.1 illustrates. At the start of the twenty-first century, healthy life expectancy was either static or *falling* in several parts of Eastern Europe (as it was in most of Sub-Saharan Africa), but was rising in Western Europe and North America.

○ Which infectious diseases have contributed most to the falling life expectancy in Eastern European and African countries?

■ HIV/AIDS and tuberculosis. (A similar decline in healthy life expectancy is also apparent in Polynesian states, and the rate of increase in most Asian and some Latin American countries has slowed or halted due to the same diseases.)

Advocates of the new public health recognize that unemployment, job insecurity and low pay are associated with shorter life-spans and higher rates of physical and mental illness. Conversely, participation in education – particularly among women – and greater equity in access to resources within a community, are associated with falling birth rates and infant mortality rates, increasing longevity and a greater proportion of the lifespan spent free from illness or disability. Thus, the new public health agenda involves action to promote employment, income support, provision of education and access to amenities such as transport, housing and health care, *as well as* improving the safety of the physical environment. It also seeks to implement the ideals of community choice and participation.

However, although the rhetoric of the new public health has great appeal, the results are uncertain. It is clear that suitable mechanisms to deliver its aims are not in place even in the wealthiest countries, in part due to inadequate knowledge of what is needed for meaningful community involvement. It is often assumed that the more people know about diseases, the more likely they are to adopt behaviours that keep them healthy. However, the evidence to support this contention is generally lacking. There is also uncertainty about how best to implement the ambitious goals of public health in the future, given the problems of sustainability to which we now turn.

4.4.2 Limits to sustainability: the condom 'gap'

The huge gulf between the health expenditures of rich and poor countries shown in Table 4.1 typifies the inequalities in resources for public health programmes all over the world. It also reflects differences in the average household incomes in developing and developed countries, and hence what individuals – as well as governments – can afford to pay to protect their health and that of their children. To illustrate this point, consider one example: the availability of condoms in areas of high HIV prevalence.

According to the WHO, the subsidised cost of 100 condoms (the number reflects a 'safety margin' above the estimated average requirement of 75 per person-year) varied in campaigns to promote condom use between US$1.50 in Cambodia and Rwanda to $17 in Brazil and Bolivia (WHO, 2000). However, millions of people in the world's poorest and most heavily HIV-infected populations subsist on less than $1 per day. But being unable to afford the price of sexual protection could be overcome if condoms are distributed free to those who need them. South Africa, for example, distributes 200 million condoms annually in an attempt to control the spread of HIV.

○ The total population of South Africa in 2000 was about 44 million, of whom roughly 30% were males in the peak age group for sexual activity (15–59 years). How many free condoms were distributed 'per man' in this age group and how does this compare with the WHO's estimate of annual requirement?

● 30% of 44 million is 13.2 million men, so the availability of free condoms for men in this age group averaged 15 per man per year, from the total of 200 million condoms distributed – 60 condoms less per man than the WHO's estimated average requirement of 75 per person-year.

South Africa is a 'middle-income' country with substantial mineral wealth and its condom distribution scheme is generously funded by comparison with other countries in Sub-Saharan Africa. However, the global manufacture of condoms supplies less than 25% of the estimated global need. The shortfall is compounded by the fact that most of the current production capacity is sold in the developed world at much higher prices than people in HIV-affected countries in Africa, Asia, South America and Eastern Europe can afford. As a result, the average availability of condoms in Sub-Saharan Africa has been estimated at less than 5 per year, per man aged 15–59 years – 13 billion condoms *less* than the annual requirement for the region (Shelton and Johnston, 2001; Myer *et al.*, 2001). Of course, even if the availability of condoms was increased to this level, HIV transmission in the region cannot be brought under control without mass behavioural change towards 'safer-sex' practices. But health education messages about safe sex could not achieve behaviour change if people who are at risk of sexually-transmitted infections do not have access to condoms.

4.4.3   Who pays?

The mass vaccination programmes described in Chapter 3 and the *Polio* Case Study are examples of public health interventions where *none* of the health-sector costs are recovered from the beneficiaries. Funds to purchase the vaccines and vaccination equipment, train and pay the staff, provide transport, cold storage, advertising, health education, record-keeping and so on, come from national governments and international agencies such as the WHO and the World Bank, and from charitable foundations and other non-governmental organisations.

The principle of **cost-free distribution** is also considered paramount to the success of some other public health strategies to control infectious diseases in the community, as in the example of free condom distribution in South Africa, Uganda, Thailand and many other countries with a rapidly growing incidence of HIV and other sexually-transmitted infections. Free 'needle-exchange' schemes have also made an impact on the transmission of HIV by injecting drug-users in many countries around the world.

○ What arguments do you think have been raised against cost-free distribution of primary-prevention products such as these?

■ There have been moral objections to supplying free condoms or drug-injecting equipment on the grounds that it could encourage sexual promiscuity, prostitution or drug addiction. Opponents have also argued that scarce resources for health care should not be diverted to fund a free distribution scheme, where a proportion of the goods will not be used at all, or not as intended, or they may be sold on for profit by the recipients.

The free supply of 'morally-neutral' products has been much less controversial – for example, the millions of free sachets of oral rehydration salts distributed at child health clinics in developing countries, to reduce the death rates from diarrhoeal diseases among young children (Figure 4.6 earlier). However, cost-free distribution can be beyond the financial means of the poorest countries, as Table 4.1 illustrated. There has also been a debate in public health circles about whether 'free' goods are used as consistently, compared with the same product when purchased by the user at a very low cost – implying that goods paid for out of one's own pocket are given more attention and value than those obtained free. It is beyond the scope of this course to discuss the evidence for either side of these arguments, but you should be aware that they are hotly contested and will not be resolved in the near future.

An alternative to cost-free distribution involves public-sector schemes that achieve some degree of 'cost recovery' by selling the goods to the consumer at a subsidised price and ploughing back the small income into supporting the scheme. Public/private partnerships have also been growing in developing countries since the mid-1990s, in particular in **social marketing** programmes. These schemes use commercial marketing strategies to promote the purchase of a socially beneficial product from private-sector suppliers at a heavily subsidised price. Market research methods identify the most attractive branding, packaging and advertising messages for locally-targeted promotional campaigns, and the guarantee of a small profit on a large volume of sales attracts private producers and distributors. Public-sector expertise harnesses donor agencies and government health organisations to subsidise the goods so they can be sold at low cost, and networks of local community leaders, shopkeepers and travelling agents aim to make the product available even in the most remote districts. In many social marketing programmes, vouchers have been issued to the poorest households to enable them to obtain the product at an even lower price.

Insecticide-treated mosquito nets

Social marketing programmes have been used in an attempt to reduce the transmission of malaria through the sale of insecticide-treated nets (ITNs) to cover beds and sleeping mats in endemic areas (as shown in Figure 1.2). The nets cost less than US$5 to manufacture and distribute, they can be sold for as little as $1 in subsidized schemes and have a lifespan of 4–5 years. In 2001, on average, only 10–15% of households in endemic areas owned a mosquito net and WHO estimated that fewer than 5% of these nets were properly treated with insecticide. 'Dipping' the net in insecticide at intervals of no more than one year (Figure 4.7) greatly increases protection against malaria.

○ Explain how ITNs directly and indirectly protect people against malaria, compared with non-insecticidal nets (reviewed on the *Malaria* CD studied in Book 1, Chapter 3).

● A person lying inside a mosquito net acts as 'bait' for the mosquitoes, attracting them onto the net. If it has been treated with insecticide, the mosquitoes die on the net, so the numbers in the room decline and this indirectly reduces the risk posed to others nearby – even people who don't have a bed-net.

FIGURE 4.7
A major problem with insecticide-treated mosquito nets is ensuring that they are regularly re-treated, but communal 'dipping' sessions can increase participation. Schemes based on village health centres and staffed by community health workers have been notably successful in Viet Nam.

Social marketing projects in various parts of Africa have increased the household ownership of mosquito nets and the correct use of insecticide re-treatment kits from 10% to around 60% of the population in the target areas. Over a three-year period, one project in rural Tanzania covering almost half a million people, achieved a 27% increase in the survival of young children to 4 years of age (Armstrong Schellenberg *et al.*, 2001). A review of similar projects to promote the use of insecticide-treated mosquito nets found an average reduction in child deaths of around 17% from all causes, (since the debilitating effects of malaria leave children more vulnerable to other infections and malnutrition), and almost 50% reduction in malarial episodes (Lengeler, 2001).

○ Despite these positive outcomes, what problems are raised by the need to re-treat mosquito nets regularly with insecticide?

● The cost of the chemicals as a regular household expense may be a deterrent and the need to repeat the task annually could easily be overlooked. Chapter 2 and the protective clothing shown in Figure 4.7 should also have alerted you to concerns about chemical toxicity if people who treat the nets do not follow the instructions correctly. And environmental pollution may occur when residual insecticide solutions are poured away.

Critics of the social marketing approach have argued that people in rural areas where malaria is endemic cannot afford to buy ITNs and re-treatment kits, and point to the rapid decline in uptake wherever cost-free distribution has been replaced by cost-recovery schemes (Curtis *et al.*, 2003). Conversely, cost-free schemes have been operating very successfully in Viet Nam for more than a decade, with significant success, as Table 4.2 shows.

TABLE 4.2 Incidence of malaria in Viet Nam, 1991 and 1998[*].

Type of case	Incidence/1991	Incidence/1998	% change
all clinically diagnosed	1.09 million	383 341	−65%
all laboratory confirmed	187 994	72 091	−62%
severe complicated	31 741	1 447	−95%
deaths	4 646	183	−96%

[*]Total population at risk: 41.9 million.

It is difficult to defend the logic of providing free measles vaccinations yet charging for ITNs, despite the rough equivalence in the cost-effectiveness of these two strategies in saving children's lives. However, the debate about 'who pays' is only one barrier to achieving the target set by the Abuja Summit meeting in April 2000 as part of the WHO's 'Roll Back Malaria' campaign. Sustainability is another serious problem. By 2005, participating governments aim to protect 60% of their populations at risk of malaria by promoting the supply and use of insecticide-treated nets and prophylactic drugs for pregnant women. The ITN target will require the production and distribution of 32 million mosquito nets and the same number of insecticide re-treatment kits every year, at an annual cost estimated at between US$ 290–320 million. Only about 10% of the requirement for ITNs is currently being met by manufacturees. Long-lasting insecticidal nets that do not require re-treatment (the chemical is bonded into the fibres) solve some of the problems outlined above, but are even more expensive.

The Abuja Summit also persuaded the governments of endemic countries to reduce or abolish all import tariffs and local taxes on the production of mosquito nets and insecticides to further reduce the price of protection for their populations. This example provides another demonstration of the breadth of public health strategies – from researching the most attractive logo to sell a cheap 'home-dipping' kit in Burkina Faso, to negotiating international trade agreements between governments and pharmaceutical manufacturers.

4.4.4   Awareness of cultural context

The provision of mosquito nets assumes that people who have them will use them, but there are cultural reasons why they may not.

☐ Can you suggest why people might be reluctant to put up mosquito nets in their houses?

▉ The nets take up a large amount of space in what can often be confined living quarters; they block access to the area above the bed, which could otherwise be used for storage; they reduce airflow, making sleeping conditions hotter; also, the nets are not aesthetically pleasing – people in malarial areas have as much pride in the appearance of their homes as people anywhere else (attempts have been made in some areas to produce nets dyed in local patterns).

This example raises the question of cultural context and how it can influence the success or failure of public health programmes. Consider another situation in which lack of awareness of cultural context has undermined initiatives to control infectious disease in the past. At the end of Section 4.2, we asked you to identify the primary prevention strategies from a list of actions that could reduce the incidence of diarrhoeal diseases in rural villages in developing countries. The list included hand-washing before preparing food and after going to the toilet, and building and using latrines. Both these strategies involve significant behavioural change by individuals, but where customary practices expose people to significant disease risks, it is often very difficult to initiate or sustain a change in behaviour (consider the difficulties in dieting or giving up smoking).

Behaviours that relate to the most intimate and private aspects of people's lives, such as their sexuality, or the practices and rituals involved in urinating or defecating, are often the most resistant to change. Moreover, new behaviours cannot be sustained without support from the community as a whole, which may only be possible if the public health project takes account of local culture.

For example, projects to construct latrines in rural villages (Figure 4.8) have sometimes found that the new facilities were not being used, even though the hygienic disposal of human excreta was understood by villagers to reduce the incidence of diarrhoeal diseases. When the reasons for non-use were investigated (Box 4.3), it became apparent that local beliefs and taboos had not been addressed by the project organisers. This example leads to the reiteration of a central tenet of the 'new public health': projects that enable communities to design their own infrastructures and agree on the conditions of usage have a greater chance of preventing infectious disease.

FIGURE 4.8

This latrine, built in 1999 as part of a health promotion project in rural villages in Peru, meets the basic standard of 'adequate sanitation' set out by the WHO. Note that 2.4 billion people do not have access to even this level of sanitation.

BOX 4.3   Reasons for not using latrines

The smell in an enclosed latrine was considered disgusting and a possible source of illness; going into a latrine identified the individual to others as engaging in a bodily function that by local custom is supposed to be conducted secretly; cultural restrictions forbade certain groups (e.g. men and women) from using the same latrines; latrines sited at any distance from a house were considered too far to use at night; small children were unable to use the latrine unaided and parents were too busy to take them; children were afraid of the dark inside the latrine shelter, or of falling into the cesspit; the faeces of babies and infants were not considered harmful so they were not put into the latrine; adults restricted their use of the latrine, or discouraged their children from using it, to avoid it filling up too fast; disposing of the contents was considered disgusting and hazardous; digging a new latrine took time and effort away from other tasks (adapted from Boot and Cairncross, 1993).

Summary of Section 4.4

1   The 'new public health' aspires to promote health as a positive attribute, beyond the absence of disease, by tackling environmental and socio-economic causes of disease, and focusing on strategies provided by multi-sectoral partnerships at the community level, with the participation of local people.

2   A positive association generally exists between spending on health by a country and the expectation of healthy life of its population.

3   Debates about the relative merits of cost-free distribution and social marketing of disease-prevention products will not be easily resolved.

4   The rhetoric of the new public health has not been matched by its outcomes. Its success is limited by lack of adequate national and personal finance for infrastructures, goods and services, by severe shortages of materials to sustain effective programmes, and by lack of awareness of the cultural context in which a programme can deliver its intended benefits.

4.5 Food poisoning in the UK

In this final section of the chapter, we return to the UK – the place where the public health movement began almost 200 years ago – to consider an important category of infectious disease and attempts to control it.

Food safety has been a major area of public health activity since the nineteenth century, directed through a system of inspection and legislation aimed at preventing sources of infectious agents and harmful chemicals or other pollutants from entering the human food chain. Food-borne infections that result in gastrointestinal symptoms such as vomiting or diarrhoea within hours (or at most 2–3 days) of eating contaminated food are referred to as **food poisoning**. The effects can range from moderate discomfort to death from multi-system organ failure.

○   What are the principal infectious agents responsible for food poisoning in Western industrialized countries (as discussed in Books 1 and 2)?

●   Certain bacteria have been identified as common causes of food poisoning, principally species of *Campylobacter, Clostridium, Salmonella, Shigella, Staphylococcus* and *E. coli* (particularly strain 0157). *Vibrio cholerae* infection is rare outside developing countries, but cases do occasionally occur. Viral causes include rotavirus (Book 1, Figure 1.9), and you may have added the Norwalk virus to the list after the highly publicized outbreaks of 'winter vomiting' in UK hospitals in recent years. A zoonotic protoctist, *Cryptosporidium*, has caused outbreaks of diarrhoeal disease in the USA (Book 2, Section 5.5.2).

4.5.1 How many cases?

Many of the pathogens involved in food poisoning can also be transmitted via other routes, for example in drinking water and directly from person to person, so it is difficult to estimate what proportion of cases are actually the result of consuming contaminated food. Another difficulty in estimating the extent of the problem is that many of the pathogens now known to cause food poisoning have only been identified in the last 20–30 years, so their incidence is 'rising' partly because new tests have been developed to detect them where none existed before (see Book 4, Chapter 3). However, even when these caveats are taken into account, there has been a substantial rise in cases of food poisoning in Western industrialized countries since the 1980s (for example, see Figure 4.9), and food safety has become a major public health concern.

☐   What explanations can you suggest for the rise in food poisoning in countries such as the UK?

●   There are many reasons (discussed in Book 1, Section 1.4), including: intensive farming practices, which have increased the bacterial contamination of raw materials used in certain foodstuffs (e.g. salmonellae in chicken and eggs); cultural changes in methods of food preparation, such as more consumption of 'cook-chill' foods re-heated in domestic microwave ovens, and a greater proportion of meals eaten in commercial premises; the global trade and transport of food and the smuggling of foodstuffs (e.g. 'bushmeat'), resulting in the importation of food-borne pathogens; and the evolution of more virulent strains of some enteric pathogens (e.g. *E. coli* 0157).

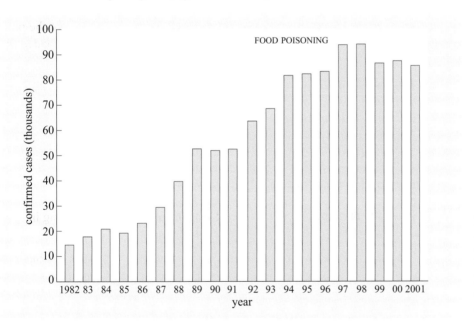

FIGURE 4.9
Number of cases of food poisoning either notified to local authorities or verified by other means, England and Wales, 1988–2001, as reported by the Public Health Laboratory Service (PHLS). The total population size was effectively stable in this period.

In the UK, food poisoning is a *notifiable disease*: under the Public Health (Infectious Disease) Regulations of 1988, all cases that reach medical attention must be reported to the environmental health officers in the local authority and to the Communicable Disease Surveillance Centre (the CDSC is a division of the Health Protection Agency). These bodies have a statutory responsibility for investigating individual cases and outbreaks of food poisoning. In a moment, we will discuss an outbreak of salmonella food poisoning among delegates at a medical conference in Wales, to give you a greater insight into the public health response in such a situation.

However, the notified cases represent only the 'tip of the iceberg' since most episodes of food poisoning go unreported. For example, annual consumer surveys by the UK's Food Standards Agency (FSA) conducted since 2000 have found that

12–14% of their respondents in England and Wales complained of experiencing food poisoning in the previous year. By extrapolation, this suggests that about 5.5 million people are affected annually.

☐ How does this estimate compare with the number of reported cases in Figure 4.9?

◼ Confirmed cases of food poisoning in England and Wales in 1999–2001 were around 86 000 annually – less than 2% of the number estimated by the FSA consumer survey.

Over 70% of the respondents in the FSA survey who had experienced an episode of food poisoning said they did not report it to anyone, and most of those who did so told only their GP (FSA, 2003). Evidence of significant under-reporting has been found in many other Western industrialized countries. For example, in the USA in recent years around 40 000 cases of food poisoning due to salmonellae have been confirmed annually, resulting in around 580 deaths; but the actual number of food-borne episodes of salmonellosis is estimated to be around 1.3 million per year (Mead *et al.*, 1999).

4.5.2 Lapses in food hygiene behaviour

The FSA was set up by an Act of Parliament in the UK in 2000 as an independent 'watchdog' to protect public health and consumer interests in relation to food. Its creation was spurred on by the epidemic of BSE in the national cattle herd and the identification of vCJD in humans, which may be caused by prions entering the human food chain in contaminated beef. Among the first targets set by the FSA were a 20% reduction in the number of cases of food-borne illness by 2006 and a 50% reduction in salmonellae in retail chicken. In 2002 the FSA conducted the largest-ever UK survey of food-hygiene knowledge among staff in small independent catering businesses. Table 4.3 shows the responses of these workers when asked to say when they washed their hands while at work.

☐ Which responses in Table 4.3 reveal the most likely sources of risk to food safety?

◼ 39% of catering staff did not report routinely washing their hands after going to the toilet, and more than half of them did not do so after handling raw meat or before preparing food. Only half reported washing their hands when they first arrived in the kitchen.

The same survey found a worrying lack of knowledge of basic principles of food safety, for example, concerning the separation of raw and cooked foods, and the temperature at which food should be stored. Even where hygiene standards are generally high (e.g. in hospital kitchens, Figure 4.10), outbreaks of food poisoning can still occur due to the breakdown of basic procedures. It is worth mentioning that many of the raw materials used in food preparation (e.g. meat, eggs, vegetables, etc.) are usually contaminated with pathogenic bacteria.

There are major difficulties in interpreting interview data on reported hygiene behaviour, since people may behave differently in 'real life', but studies that compare self-reports with observer-recorded measures generally find that hygiene behaviours occur even *less* often than respondents claim. Around 70% of the

TABLE 4.3 Responses of catering workers asked about hand-washing at work.*

When do you wash your hands?	%
after every job	62
after going to the toilet	61
when coming into the kitchen	50
after handling raw meat	48
before preparing food	47
after preparing food	37
after handling cooked meat	31
when they are dirty	21
when leaving the kitchen	19
after handling money	17
after a cigarette	17
after washing up	16
after handling fruit and veg	15

*Based on a survey of 1016 UK catering managers and staff in 2002.

FIGURE 4.10
Hospital kitchens have a particular responsibility to observe food-hygiene practices; outbreaks of food poisoning among patients can result in ward closures and occasionally deaths.

consumers in the FSA survey (mentioned earlier) who had experienced an episode of food poisoning, attributed it to food prepared outside the home, but lapses in hygiene behaviour in domestic food-handling are also common.

Enforcement of public health regulations on food standards in the UK is primarily the responsibility of local authorities, through the Environmental Health and Trading Standards Officers. Meat production and dairy hygiene are (respectively) the responsibility of the Meat Hygiene Service and the Hygiene Inspectorate. The FSA reported that about 700 000 food premises in the UK were visited by health inspectors in 2001, of which 175 000 failed the inspection. Most UK local authorities in 2002 were only carrying out just over 50% of planned inspections of high-risk food businesses. Health inspectors can take a range of actions if they detect lapses in the required procedures to protect the public from food-borne diseases, principally:

- Written warnings (issued in 95% of cases)
- Improvement notices (6350 issued in 2001)
- Formal cautions
- Emergency prohibition notices
- Seizure of goods
- Prosecutions (655 in 2001)
- Permanent prohibition orders.

Common lapses in food-safety procedures are illustrated by a well-documented outbreak of salmonella food poisoning, which also gives an insight into how the public health officials went about tracing its source.

4.5.3 Food poisoning at a medical conference

> Before commencing this section, we suggest that you refresh your knowledge of the bacteria that cause salmonellosis from Book 2, Section 2.6.4. You may also find it useful to read Book 6, Section 1.2 again to revise the calculation of infection risk.

The day after a buffet lunch eaten during a medical conference in Cardiff in 1986, twenty-three delegates were admitted to hospital suffering from severe diarrhoea (lasting nine days on average), fever and muscular and abdominal pains. Food from the buffet was eaten by 266 delegates; over the next few days, 196 of them developed symptoms of food poisoning (Figure 4.11) and several more were hospitalized (32 in all). It was estimated that the cost to the NHS in time lost from work by the sick delegates and time spent by other doctors in caring for them was more than 1600 'doctor-days' over a three-week period. The investigation of this outbreak was reported in the academic press with unusual thoroughness (Palmer *et al.*, 1990), perhaps because the victims were members of the medical profession.

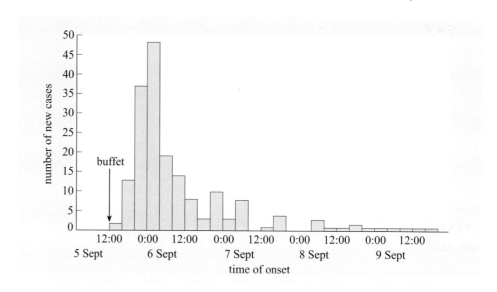

FIGURE 4.11
Time-course of onset of 196 cases of food poisoning relative to eating food from a buffet at a medical conference; the width of each bar represents a four-hour period.

When samples of the delegates' faeces were cultured on agar plates (the technique was shown in association with Book 4, in a video clip on the *Reference* CD), colonies were identified and *Salmonella typhimurium* DT9 was detected (there are over 2200 serotypes of *Salmonella* which can cause disease in humans). The speed of onset of symptoms can also provide a pointer to the type of bacterial infection involved; in food poisoning due to staphylococci, symptoms usually commence in 1–6 hours, salmonellae in 6–72 hours (as Figure 4.11 shows), and clostridia in one to several days.

○ Calculate the infection risk for delegates who attended the buffet. (If you are unsure how to do this, revise Book 6, Section 1.2.)

● Of the 266 who attended the buffet, 196 (74%) became ill, so the infection risk = 0.74.

Infection with samonellae is usually self-limiting, although 32 of the patients in this outbreak were admitted to hospital for an average of four days. Treatment with antibacterials is not usually advisable because they do not reduce symptoms or shorten the illness. In fact, drug treatment may prolong excretion of salmonellae in the faeces and it can also encourage the development of resistance. (Interestingly, however, in this outbreak 37 doctors received antibacterial therapy, although in all cases without benefit according to the report by Palmer *et al.* in the *Journal of the Royal College of Physicians of London.*)

In order to identify the cause of the food poisoning, a questionnaire was sent to delegates to determine the various foods eaten at the buffet and whether the risk of becoming ill was associated with certain dishes. The results are shown in Table 4.4. The **relative risk** in this example is calculated from:

$$\frac{\text{the risk of illness in those eating a certain food}}{\text{the risk of illness in those who did not eat it}}$$

Therefore, if the food has no effect, the relative risk should equal 1. Values greater than 1 suggest that eating the food could be a risk factor for the illness.

TABLE 4.4 Attack rates for delegates eating and not eating specific foods.

Food	Eaten			Not eaten			Relative risk
	ill	total no.	% ill	ill	total no.	% ill	
tuna	70	98	72	127	169	76	0.9
ham	48	63	77	149	204	73	1.1
beef	29	46	64	168	221	76	0.8
salmon	38	46	84	159	221	72	1.2
egg mayonnaise	67	89	76	130	178	73	1.0
pate	50	66	76	147	201	74	1.0
beef sandwiches	10	13	79	187	254	75	1.1
ham sandwiches	15	20	75	182	247	74	1.0
chicken	182	213	86	15	54	29	3.0*
quiche (cheese)	80	108	50	117	159	74	0.7
quiche (ham)	18	21	86	179	246	73	1.2
ham & turkey pie	103	137	76	94	130	73	1.0

* $p <<< 0.01$

○ From the data in Table 4.4, which food is most likely to have caused the outbreak of food poisoning? How confident do you feel about your answer and why?

● The judgement is not completely straightforward, since many different foods are likely to have been eaten by any one delegate. However, the only foodstuff with a relative risk much greater than 1 was chicken (i.e. a high number of delegates who ate it became ill, but only a few people who did not eat it were affected). Statistical analysis showed that chicken was the only foodstuff where the results were highly significant ($p < 0.01$; probability values were discussed in Chapter 2, see Box 2.6).

This result demonstrates the importance of conducting statistical analyses in evaluating the outcomes of public health studies. But caution must always be taken in interpreting the results. For example, Table 4.4 shows that the relative risk of food poisoning for those eating cheese quiche, beef and tuna was *less* than 1, i.e. people who ate these foods were less likely to become ill than people who did not eat them. However, we cannot assume that eating these foods 'protects' people from salmonellae – a more plausible explanation is that people who chose the cheese quiche, beef or tuna simply did not eat any of the chicken.

The environmental health officers and other investigating authorities were able to confirm that the chicken was the cause of the outbreak: cultures from unused chickens taken from the refrigerator the day after the buffet were found to be contaminated with 2.8 million *S. typhimurium* DT9 organisms per gram of meat. Box 4.4 describes how the chickens for the buffet were prepared.

BOX 4.4   **Preparation of chickens causing an outbreak of salmonellosis**

Day 1: 50 deep-frozen chickens were laid out on tables at room temperature to thaw overnight;

Day 2: they were cut into pieces and steam cooked for 45 minutes, left to cool in the steamer, then removed and left to stand at room temperature for 2 hours, before refrigerating for 2 hours. The chicken pieces were then coated with egg and breadcrumbs and packed into roasting trays (a task that took 1.5 hours at room temperature), and refrigerated again;

Day 3: (the day of the conference) the chicken pieces were oven roasted for 30–40 minutes at high temperature, then put into a refrigerated larder until served at the lunch buffet.

(Details from Palmer *et al.*, 1990)

☐ What circumstances allowed the salmonellae to replicate to pathogenic levels, as suggested by the sequence in Box 4.4?

◖ The frozen chickens were thawed two days before they were eaten and thereafter the meat was heated and cooled several times, and left to stand for long periods at room temperature – creating favourable conditions for bacterial replication (the optimum doubling time for salmonellae is about 20 minutes, but it varies under 'real life' conditions).

This example illustrates a number of themes raised several times in this chapter. The protection of public health relies on a combination of properly maintained infrastructures (in this case, the kitchen equipment), adequate staff training and health education (e.g. in food-hygiene behaviour), a surveillance system to track the outbreak and make the link between cases, an inspection regime to ensure compliance with legislation and standards (on food handling and microbial content), and a community that supports good practice (in the kitchen). Economic constraints are likely to be a significant factor in the level of infection risk posed by commercially prepared food, just as they are in other arenas that affect public health.

In the final chapter of this book, we present a case study on the control of guinea worm disease – a parasitic infection that might seem, in prospect, to have nothing in common with food poisoning. But as you will see, the campaign to achieve the global eradication of this disease also relies on properly maintained infrastructures (water wells and filters), health education by trained staff (on how to interrupt the parasite's life-cycle), a surveillance system to map cases, an inspection regime to ensure compliance with prevention procedures, and a community that supports good practice.

Summary of Section 4.5

1   Food poisoning is a growing cause of diarrhoeal disease in the UK; cases should be notified to the public health authorities, but perhaps as few as 2% are reported.

2   Common lapses in food-hygiene behaviour that pose a significant infection risk to consumers involve poor hand hygiene, inadequate separation of raw and cooked foods, and food stored at incorrect temperatures for long periods.

3   Food safety (like other areas of concern for public health) relies on the provision of adequate infrastructures, effective staff training, health education, surveillance, enforcement of legislation, and a community that supports good practice.

Learning outcomes for Chapter 4

When you have studied this chapter you should be able to:

4.1   Define and use, or recognize definitions and applications of, each of the terms printed in **bold** in the text. *(Questions 4.1–4.4)*

4.2   Consider a range of public health strategies, including unfamiliar examples presented to you, and identify the levels of prevention (primary, secondary, tertiary) and the levels of intervention (individual, community, national, international) involved in them. *(Question 4.1)*

4.3   Summarize the traditional focus of the public health movement and describe the features of the 'new public health' *(Question 4.2)*

4.4   Demonstrate an awareness of circumstances that may limit the achievement of public health goals, including economic constraints, issues of access and sustainability, debates about who pays for services and awareness of cultural context. *(Question 4.3)*

4.5   Use or analyse examples of public health interventions to illustrate the importance of community participation and community health workers in controlling infectious disease. *(Questions 4.3 and 4.4)*

4.6   Describe common sources of infection risk in relation to food handling and the disposal of human excreta, and discuss strategies that may protect public health from diarrhoeal diseases. *(Question 4.4)*

Questions for Chapter 4

Question 4.1

What measures can be taken to control malaria at each of the primary, secondary and tertiary levels of prevention? (This question builds on your knowledge of the *Malaria* Case Study, as well as on material in Chapters 2 and 4 of this book.)

Question 4.2

In what ways could the TB sanitaria of the late nineteenth and early twentieth century be said to reflect traditional public health approaches to the control of infectious disease? To what extent does the present day DOTs programme meet the criteria of the 'new public health' movement?

Question 4.3

In a rural area of Egypt, where local people knew that entering the local canal carried a significant risk of infection with schistosoma parasites, the majority of women took their family's clothing to wash in the canal even though there were stand-pipes in the village. The only means of disposing of waste water from washing clothes in the village was either to pour it onto the ground between the houses (which were made of mud bricks), or to tip it into the latrines. What factors may have influenced the women's decision to risk infection by going to the canal rather than wash clothes in the village?

Question 4.4

Consider the position of Uganda in Table 4.1 and in Figure 4.6, relative to the other countries shown in these sources. What does this comparison suggest about the ability of poor countries to protect the health of their populations from infectious disease? What agencies would you expect to be involved in achieving progress?

GUINEA WORM: A CASE STUDY

5

During this final case study, you will spend about one hour on an Internet investigation of the WHO's Public Health Mapping project, which has mapped the location of all the villages in Sub-Saharan Africa where guinea worm disease is still endemic. This mapping project is a key part of the coordinated 'search and containment' programme that aims to eradicate *Dracunculus medinensis* globally through relatively low-cost, low-technology public health interventions.

5.1 The little dragon of Medina

Guinea worm disease or **dracunculiasis** is caused by a nematode worm, *Dracunculus medinensis* – literarily the 'little dragon of Medina' – the largest tissue parasite to affect humans. The association of the worm with a dragon may be due to the fiery burning pain experienced at the site where the worm emerges from the body, usually in the lower leg or foot. Like smallpox, it has been known since antiquity and evidence of guinea worms has been found in Egyptian mummies. The practice of 'winding' the emerging worm onto a stick (Figure 5.1), which has been practised for at least two thousand years, may even have given rise to the symbolic emblem of the medical profession – a staff entwined by two serpents. The prominence of this parasite in medical texts from many parts of the ancient world testifies to its global importance as a cause of human disability in the past. We have chosen it for the final case study in this course because the campaign that has brought it to the edge of eradication illustrates many of the key features of the public health approach to controlling infectious diseases, and many of the problems in sustaining an eradication programme.

The terms 'dracunculiasis' and 'guinea worm disease' are used interchangeably in the literature on this condition; you will also find 'Guinea worm' capitalized in some sources.

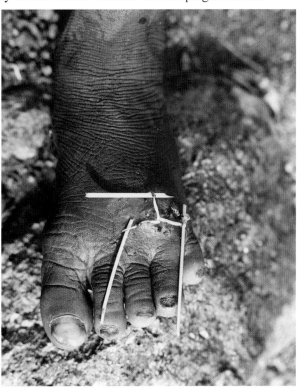

FIGURE 5.1
Three guinea worms (*Dracunculus medinensis*) emerging from a Sudanese child's foot have been wound around sticks in an attempt to reduce the painful period until they fall out completely. Adult worms can reach 0.5–1.0 m in length and take around six weeks to emerge.

5.2 The transmission cycle

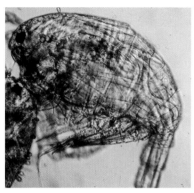

FIGURE 5.2
An aquatic crustacean, *Mesocyclops*, known as cyclops, measuring about 0.8 mm in length, with infective larvae of *Dracunculus medinensis* inside the body cavity.

Dracunculiasis is the only human disease in which the causative agent is transmitted exclusively in drinking water. The life cycle of *D. medinensis* involves a larval maturation stage in an intermediate host – microscopic fresh-water crustacea referred to in the infectious-disease literature as 'cyclops'. (Until recently, all the species that transmit guinea worm larvae were classified in a single genus, *Cyclops*, which has since been subdivided, but for simplicity we will use the traditional term.) People become infected when they drink water contaminated with cyclops containing infective dranunculus larvae (Figure 5.2). The larvae are released in the person's stomach when the cyclops is killed by the acid environment. Over a period of about three months, the larvae migrate out of the gut into the thorax and mature into sexually differentiated male and female worms of a few centimetres in length. The male dies after mating, but the female continues growing for the next 8–12 months, reaching 0.5–1.0 m in length. She migrates along muscle fascia towards the surface of the body, usually somewhere in the lower limbs, often on the ankles or feet, where the worm slowly emerges and sheds immature larvae into sources of drinking water. The larvae are eaten by cyclops, initiating another cycle of infection (Figure 5.3).

FIGURE 5.3
The transmission cycle of *Dracunculus medinensis* takes about one year. As mature female worms emerge from their human host, they shed millions of larvae when exposed to cold water. The larvae are eaten by aquatic cyclops, mature quickly into the infective stage and are ingested by people in contaminated drinking water. Worm larvae reach sexual maturity in the connective tissues in about three months. Males die after mating, but females grow for 8–12 months and migrate along muscle fascia to emerge, shed their larvae and so repeat the cycle.

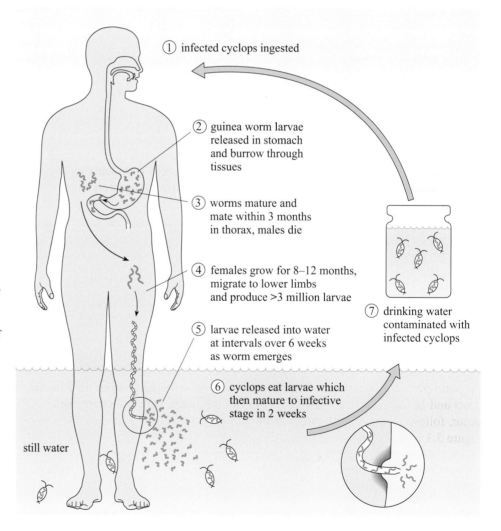

① infected cyclops ingested

② guinea worm larvae released in stomach and burrow through tissues

③ worms mature and mate within 3 months in thorax, males die

④ females grow for 8–12 months, migrate to lower limbs and produce >3 million larvae

⑤ larvae released into water at intervals over 6 weeks as worm emerges

⑥ cyclops eat larvae which then mature to infective stage in 2 weeks

⑦ drinking water contaminated with infected cyclops

still water

Although dracunculus species are known to infect reptiles and large mammals in areas where guinea worm disease is endemic in humans, there is no evidence that these animals have ever acted as a reservoir for parasites in the human population. Dracunculiasis is therefore not considered to be a zoonotic disease. Over thousands of years, *D. medinensis* has become well adapted to survive in its human host for a period averaging 12 months, apparently without inducing an immune response against the adult worm. The surface antigens of the worms do not appear to be immunogenic and it does little harm to its host during the maturation period.

○ What are the consequences of the lack of an immune response against adult worms for people in endemic areas?

● A positive consequence is that they do not suffer the cell-mediated tissue damage that characterizes the immune response to some other chronic infections (Book 3, Section 4.2 refers to chronic hypersensitivity reactions, e.g. in leprosy). But in the absence of an immune response, memory cells that recognize worm antigens are not formed and there is no protective immunity against subsequent infection. Thus, the same individual can become reinfected year after year.

The worms have evolved a further adaptation, which increases the chance of transmission from their definitive host (human) to their intermediate host (cyclops) by exploiting the innate protective mechanisms that generate inflammation at an infection site. A mature female worm carries over three million immature larvae. As it nears the surface of the human tissue from which it is about to emerge, the worm releases a burst of larvae just under the host's skin. The larvae are strongly immunogenic and provoke a rapid inflammatory response, which erupts in an intensely painful fluid-filled ulcer, usually somewhere on the lower limbs. No other parasite that infects humans behaves like *D. medinensis*, so there is no ambiguity about the diagnosis at this point.

A natural response to the burning pain of the ulcer is to cool it by standing in cold water – and in rural communities this is most commonly a village pond, or a shallow 'step well' where people step down into the water to fill drinking pots. The sudden cooling stimulates the worm to emerge by a few millimetres and release several thousand immature larvae into the water. Over the next six weeks, the worm emerges slowly, releasing another shower of larvae every time it is exposed to cool water. The worm larvae are free swimming and can survive for several days in still ponds and shallow wells, which are also ideal habitats for the cyclops. These predatory crustaceans cannot reach the population density required for effective transmission of guinea worm larvae in fast-running streams or deep wells. And because the cyclops are only about 0.8 mm in length, they go undetected in unfiltered drinking water, which is frequently contaminated with other sources of organic matter. In every country there is a seasonal peak of 2–3 months (usually in the main period of agricultural activity) in which worms emerge from their human hosts and larvae are shed into sources of drinking water. New infections then occur, followed by the long unseen maturation period before the cycle shown in Figure 5.3 is again repeated one year later.

Summary of Section 5.2

1   Guinea worm disease is caused by a nematode worm *Dracunculus medinensis*. There are no known reservoirs of infection in other vertebrates.

2   Over a period of about six weeks, larvae are shed into sources of drinking water by female worms emerging (usually) from the lower limbs; they emerge seasonally over a relatively short period of 2–3 months.

3   Infection occurs when people drink water contaminated with cyclops, the microscopic aquatic crustaceans that act as the intermediate host for worm larvae.

4   Protective immunity does not develop, so re-infection of the same individuals can occur year after year.

5.3 The human cost of dracunculiasis

By the middle of the twentieth century, dracunculiasis had already disappeared (largely spontaneously) from many parts of the world where it had once been endemic, including North Africa, Egypt, Iraq, Brazil, the West Indies and Uzbekistan. It was confined to parts of the Indian subcontinent, Middle Eastern countries such as the Yemen and Iran, and rural areas of Sub-Saharan Africa, where over 50 million people suffered its effects each year. However, it was neglected as a public health issue largely because it is rarely fatal, permanent disability is unusual and infected people generally recover within a few weeks of the worm's emergence. Until the 1980s, the international health agencies attached a low priority to this 'forgotten disease of forgotten people'.

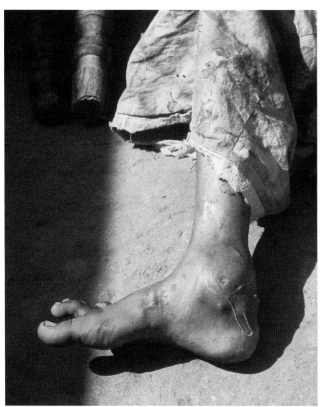

However, attitudes gradually changed as a number of research studies evaluated the human cost of a disease with a global burden estimated in 1986 to be affecting at least 3.3 million people. Although the case fatality rate is under 0.1% (death is usually caused by a secondary tetanus infection) and permanent disability is rare, many microbes can infect the lesion caused where the worm emerges and they can penetrate deep into the tissues along the track of the worm (Figure 5.4). Around half of all cases become infected, which greatly increases the disabling effects of the parasite, both in terms of pain in the affected limb which can reduce mobility for several weeks, and the fever, nausea and debility associated with an acute inflammatory reaction and secondary bacterial infection. More serious complications occur in about 1% of cases and include worms emerging into joints and triggering severe arthritis, or emerging from the breast, genitals, tongue or eye.

FIGURE 5.4
Inflammation due to a secondary bacterial infection along the track of an emergent guinea worm can be seen in the ankle of this woman, photographed in Pakistan.

☐ Suggest how guinea worm infection could have a serious impact on rural communities.

⬤ An immobilizing condition impacts heavily on rural economies where people earn their livelihoods from working on the land; they often walk long distances to reach their fields, herd livestock, collect firewood and drinking water, and – in the case of children – attend school.

Various studies have recorded the loss of agricultural productivity in rural economies where dracunculiasis remains endemic, and have measured the consequences in terms of 'stunting' among children whose diet has been impoverished as a result. In Mali, the local name for dracunculiasis is 'the disease of the empty granary'. The economic impact is particularly severe because the highest rates of infection occur in the rural working population (15–45 year-olds), who are the most likely to be exposed to contaminated water in the natural pools they drink from while working in the fields. People are less at risk from drinking water taken from deep wells and boreholes, which are more likely to be located within villages; the provision of piped water in towns and cities eliminated the disease from urban locations decades ago.

None of the drugs used in the treatment of other parasitic worms has any therapeutic effect in people infected with guinea worms. At most they are given antibacterial ointment to reduce the risk of secondary infections, or antibacterial drugs in more severe cases. Surgical removal of the worm, though practiced in some countries, is strongly discouraged by WHO, because it is often ineffective and increases the risk of secondary bacterial infection. No vaccine has yet been developed to protect people who ingest the larvae, since the worms are not immunogenic and there is no understanding of what an effective immune response would be. Thus, attempts to control dracunculiasis must rely on non-medical interventions.

Summary of Section 5.3

1   Emerging worms generally cause temporary disability, due to painful inflammatory reactions, nausea, fever and secondary bacterial infections, which often prevent affected people from working or attending school. This has severe consequences for agricultural production, local economies and educational progress.

2   There are no effective drugs or surgical treatments for guinea worm disease and it cannot be prevented by vaccination.

5.4 The global eradication campaign

The recognition of the seriousness of the guinea worm problem led the Indian government to initiate the first national dracunculiasis elimination programme in 1982. Similar programmes began later in Pakistan, Cameroon, Ghana and Nigeria, and in 1989 the WHO launched the global eradication campaign.

☐ Consider all the information presented so far in this case study. What features of dracunculiasis suggest that a global eradication campaign is feasible, despite the lack of drugs to kill the worms in the body or a protective vaccine?

1   The disease has died out spontaneously in many parts of the world, suggesting that the transmission cycle can be interrupted.

2   There is no other mammalian host for *D. medinensis* to act as a reservoir of infection.

3   The intermediate host (cyclops) is restricted to still water in shallow pools and step wells, so it cannot extend its range (in contrast to an insect vector).

4   Infected people are easily identified at the point when a worm is emerging; there is no ambiguity about the diagnosis.

5   The period in which an infected person poses a risk to others is relatively short (about six weeks while the worm emerges).

6   Transmission to humans is exclusively in drinking water, so if local water sources can be protected from contamination by worm larvae, the infection cycle could be broken.

7   The worm larvae are shed seasonally, over a predictable period of 2–3 months, so interventions can be focused intensively at certain times.

These features underlie the strategies that have been most successful in eliminating guinea worms from many countries and greatly reducing the incidence in the remaining endemic areas. The campaign illustrates several features of the public health approach to the control of infectious diseases, particularly in remote regions with high levels of poverty and low literacy rates. It has relied primarily on two simple, low-technology strategies, operated within the affected communities by local people:

•   the routine filtering of water before drinking to remove the infected cyclops;

•   the protection of drinking-water sources from re-infection by persuading people with emerging worms not to enter the water until the lesion has healed.

In more recent years, case containment has also been practised in the later stages of a campaign (it is too labour intensive to be used on a large scale). It involves the controlled release of worm larvae by plunging the affected limb into a bucket of cold water, followed by simple palliative treatment (e.g. painkillers, antibiotic ointment), and bandaging of the worm-emergence site. The infected person agrees not to remove the bandage or enter sources of drinking water, and the procedure is repeated every few days until the worm has completely emerged.

The filtration of drinking water has been supported by the donation from the manufacturer of hundreds of thousands of square metres of a fine mesh nylon cloth, at a cost of US$14 million. Squares of cloth can be placed over the neck of containers when water is poured for drinking; it is long lasting and easily washed, which has helped greatly in popularizing the use of these simple filters. Short pieces of small diameter plastic pipe with one end covered in fine cloth have also been supplied as drinking straws. A string attached at the open end enables the straw to be hung around the neck, so workers can take it with them to the fields to use when they drink from shallow pools during the day.

The health education messages and the case containment strategy have largely been delivered by one or two volunteers from each village, each given basic training and provided with a few educational aids (e.g. posters, leaflets, slogans on T-shirts, as illustrated later in Figure 5.10) to raise understanding of how the guinea worm larvae were transmitted and how to prevent re-infection. They often check on the use of filter cloths and the protection of ponds. Regional teams supervise the community health workers and report to the national registry, which collates all the data and reports cases and containment rates to the WHO.

Since it began, the global dracunculiasis eradication programme has made huge progress (see Figure 5.5), achieving a 95% reduction in case reports between 1989 and 2001. However, the initial target date for global eradication of 1995 proved far too optimistic – a situation that often happens in large-scale disease control campaigns. The target needs to be 'soon enough' to motivate governments, donor agencies and local health teams, but not so unrealistic that the whole campaign is thrown into disrepute. The new target date is 2005, so the race is on to see which disease will be the second (after smallpox) to achieve eradication status – dracunculiasis or polio.

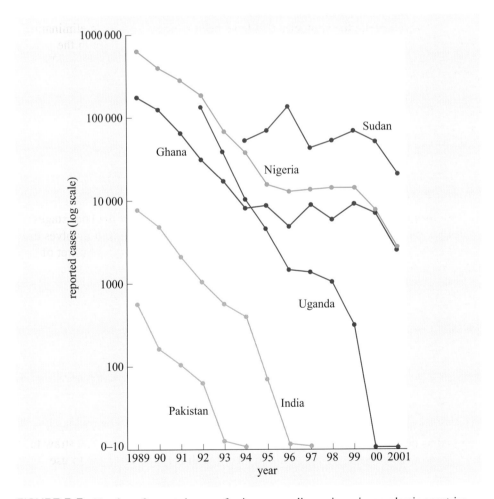

FIGURE 5.5   Number of reported cases of guinea worm disease in various endemic countries, 1989 to 2001. Note that the vertical axis has a logarithmic scale.

Of the countries shown in Figure 5.5 (see back), Pakistan and India were certified by the WHO as free of dracunculiasis in 1997 and 2000 respectively, and Uganda was one of five countries in the pre-certification surveillance phase in 2002, which requires a minimum of three consecutive years with no cases reported by a reliable surveillance system. All of the 13 remaining endemic countries are in Africa. In the whole of 2001, there were 63 717 cases reported globally, of which 49 471 (78% of the total) were in the Sudan, where eradication efforts have been disrupted by the long civil war. Nigeria and Ghana each reported around 5000 cases, and Togo and Burkina Faso around 1000 cases each; the remaining eight endemic countries collectively reported only a few hundred cases. (The data for 2001 are reported and analysed fully in the WHO's *Weekly Epidemiological Record*, No.18, May 2002.) Figure 5.6 shows the country status published by the WHO in May 2002.

Of course, the most effective way to eradicate dracunculiasis would be to provide safe drinking water, which would also reduce the risk of many other important infectious diseases such as cholera, infective hepatitis, typhoid, polio and diarrhoeal diseases, which are also endemic in the same geographical locations. In the early years of the global eradication campaign, considerable emphasis was placed on improving water quality by drilling boreholes and installing a hand-pump in villages in endemic areas, but the cost (about US$10 000 each) was unsustainable from government funds, even with aid donations. Also, the pumps need regular maintenance and many have fallen into disuse, particularly when they have to be sited some distance from a village, or where they cannot be used in the dry season

certified free   not yet certified

pre-certificate   endemic countries

FIGURE 5.6   Status of the global dracunculiasis eradication campaign in May 2002. Countries 'not yet certified' have not reported any cases for several years, but existing surveillance mechanisms are deemed insufficiently reliable to detect and report all cases. Those in 'pre-certification surveillance' have reliable case detection and reporting systems and will be certified free of transmission if no cases occur for at least three consecutive years.

because the water table falls too low (Figure 5.7). And there are many villages where the provision of boreholes is not feasible for geological reasons, or where a semi-nomadic lifestyle takes people away from the village for long periods each year.

FIGURE 5.7
This borehole was drilled and fitted with a water pump as part of the guinea worm elimination campaign in Nigeria, but it has fallen into disrepair. It is placed midway between four villages, so responsibility for maintaining it is unclear; everyone has a long walk to reach it, and no water can be raised in the dry season.

Studies comparing villages where boreholes were (or were not) drilled, showed that very considerable reductions in case reports were achievable through behaviour change alone, where the health education messages about filtering drinking water and not re-infecting the water sources were being delivered effectively. Figure 5.8 shows the results of a longitudinal study in Nigeria, among several others that persuaded health authorities in endemic countries that much could be achieved without huge expenditure on water systems which they could not afford. Cheaper 'draw wells' can be constructed in some areas to avoid people having to stand in the water whilst it is extracted.

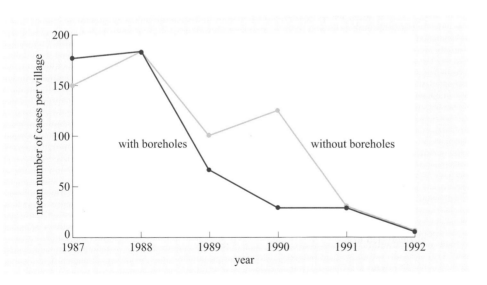

FIGURE 5.8   The average number of cases of dracunculiasis reported annually from 1987 to 1992 in 77 Nigerian villages in Enugu State with boreholes and health education campaigns to prevent transmission, compared to case reports from 30 villages with health education as the sole intervention.

In the 1990s, some additional help in the final stages of an elimination campaign has come from the donation of a water-treatment chemical (temephos), which can be added safely to drinking water to kill infected cyclops, provided the volume of water can be accurately measured. At the correct concentration temephos is harmless to fish or humans, but its application is labour intensive and accurate dosing is a major problem. Figure 5.9 illustrates the difficulty of dosing a natural pond effectively, when the water volume can change rapidly with the seasons and the chemical treatment must be repeated at least once a month.

FIGURE 5.9
Dosing a pond with temephos to kill cyclops, as here in Nigeria, presents considerable difficulties in estimating the volume of water accurately as it fluctuates over time. The process must be repeated every month and villagers may still be infected from many untreated smaller pools in the area.

Summary of Section 5.4

1   The transmission cycle can be interrupted by filtering drinking water and persuading people not to enter water sources while worms are emerging.

2   Case containment has become increasingly important, involving controlled release of larvae, palliative care and bandaging of worm-emergence sites, coupled with health education to protect local water sources.

3   The global eradication programme has reduced case reports by over 95% since 1989, largely through the efforts of volunteer community health workers with simple training and low-technology equipment (e.g. filter cloths) – much of it donated by manufacturers.

4   The 13 remaining endemic countries in 2002 were all in Africa; over 75% of all cases globally were in the Sudan, where the eradication campaign has been unable to progress as quickly due to the long civil war.

5.5 Public health mapping

Accurate reporting of cases to a central registry is a vital element in the progress of local, regional and national elimination campaigns and in the targeting of interventions in areas of need. Passive surveillance identifies patients who visit health clinics and will pick up only about 2.5% of cases. But the network of community health workers proved to be an effective resource for data collection – at least while substantial numbers of cases were being identified (a point we return to in the next section).

In 1993, in order to facilitate the identification of all 'villages of endemicity' where transmission of guinea worms was occurring, the WHO began to develop **public health mapping**, using remote sensing by commercial satellites and Geographic Information Systems (GIS) software. At regional level, public health officials were trained to input the data so it could be continually updated. This technology has enabled data to be combined on a visual display, which maps the exact locations of at-risk populations, natural water sources, relevant infrastructures (e.g. wells, boreholes, health clinics, schools), and the number of trained health workers committed to guinea worm elimination projects. The maps allowed the swift identification of places where resources were being targeted effectively, and where there were gaps in provision, or where cases were being imported from neighbouring areas. In this respect, they are the modern equivalent of John Snow's 1859 map of cholera cases around the Broad Street pump in London (see the *Cholera* Case Study). Moreover, the dracunculiasis maps have proved highly effective advocacy tools, both for informing governments of the progress of the campaign and for persuading commercial donors and aid agencies to support it.

Subsequently, the public health mapping project has been extended to support other eradication and disease control programmes, including the Polio Eradication Campaign and 'Roll Back Malaria'. In 2003, the system was extended to HIV and other sexually-transmitted infections, tuberculosis, and complex emergency situations involving infectious diseases.

> Before completing your study of this book, you should aim to spend about one hour on an Internet exploration of the WHO's Public Health Mapping projects, beginning with the dracunculiasis maps and then branching out into whichever maps interest you most. The website address can be found by following the link under 'Course Resources' on the course website.

5.6 Problems in sustaining momentum

The practical problems associated with dracunculiasis elimination campaigns in various countries reveal some of the key difficulties in sustaining public health approaches to infectious disease control. Perhaps the least problematic aspect has been to convince villagers in endemic areas that releasing larvae into a pond can cause guinea worm disease one year later. Despite initial scepticism among professional health educators, the efforts of local volunteers to support behaviour change in local populations have generally exceeded expectations, even in remote rural communities with poor literacy rates and several spoken languages (Figure 5.10).

FIGURE 5.10
Flip-charts with simple diagrams and T-shirts reinforcing health education messages have helped community health workers to interrupt the transmission of guinea worm disease by promoting behaviour change in rural communities. Here, Dr Sam Bugri, the campaign leader in Ghana, shows some teaching aids.

The most serious difficulty has been the inability to maintain the programme in areas of southern Sudan where the civil war has been most intense. More than one-third of the endemic villages failed to submit any case reports in 2001, despite abundant evidence that transmission of guinea worms was still extensive.

○ Suggest an additional problem that the war in Sudan presents for the global eradication campaign.

■ The movement of refugees fleeing from the war across the border into neighbouring countries imports new infectious cases of guinea worm disease, which are difficult to track as people disperse into the countryside. As a result, it is impossible to award 'disease-free' certification to countries bordering the Sudan, even when no indigenous cases have been reported for several years (e.g. as in Kenya).

Another problem has been irregular funding for personnel and resources. For example, since the donation of nylon cloth for filters ended in 1998, some countries have struggled to meet the cost of replacement as existing supplies wear out. Lack of trained engineers and money to buy replacement parts underlie the failure to maintain water pumps in good repair. Inadequate surveillance in poorly organized campaigns leads to ineffective intervention in the peak period for transmission, allowing the disease to re-emerge very rapidly, as occurred in Mali in 2001 when case reports rose by 151% compared with the previous year.

○ What do you think is the most difficult period to sustain the momentum of an elimination campaign?

● It gets much harder to motivate volunteer health workers as the number of cases detected falls to a low level; if the peak period in one year passes without finding a single case, there may be little incentive to look systematically for cases the following year. Similarly, governments who have allocated scarce funding to the eradication campaign may decide to divert money to other, apparently more pressing, health problems once the incidence of dracunculiasis has dwindled.

In most countries, as the number of cases detected has fallen, it has been necessary to offer incentives to infected people to participate in case containment programmes. Although there has been a slight concern that paying people to come forward could encourage them to seek out a source of infection, there is no evidence that this has occurred. On the contrary, the incidence of the disease is more likely to rise in areas where incentive schemes have been abandoned.

We conclude by drawing attention to an ethical problem of a very different kind. As the deliberately targeted extinction of *D. medinensis* approaches, there are concerns about the inadequate biological characterisation of a species that will soon be eradicated. Very few female worms have been collected in a suitable condition for research and no males have ever been recovered from humans. The 4th meeting of the International Commission for the Certification of Dracunculiasis Eradication (WHO/CDS/CPE/CEE, 2000) recommended that strenuous efforts be made to collect intact specimens and send them to European laboratories for genome sequence analysis and the preservation of a *D. medinensis* gene library before it is too late.

Summary of Section 5.6

1 The main challenge to the eradication of dracunculiasis is warfare and civil unrest in endemic areas, which disrupts surveillance and intervention, and transports infection across borders as refugees flee their homes.

2 Other difficulties are due to lack of funding and other resources to sustain the intervention programme, and dwindling motivation as the number of cases falls to a low level. The re-emergence of dracunculiasis can occur very rapidly in these circumstances.

Learning outcomes for Chapter 5

When you have studied this chapter you should be able to:

5.1 Define and use, or recognize definitions and applications of, each of the terms printed in **bold** in the text.

5.2 Describe the transmission cycle of *D. medinensis*, identify features that facilitate its interruption and discuss interventions that have been effective in preventing infection. *(Question 5.1)*

5.3 Discuss strategies that have been important in progressing the global dracunculiasis eradication campaign and the factors that could undermine its success. *(Questions 5.1 and 5.2)*

Questions for Chapter 5

Question 5.1

Explain why the type of water source available is a key factor in determining 'areas of endemicity' for dracunculiasis.

Question 5.2

What strategies could be employed to alter the association between the type of water source and dracunculiasis, and what are the main problems in sustaining them?

Links to the online sources for this case study are listed under *Course Resources* on the S320 website.

REFERENCES

Note: the websites listed below were last accessed in May 2003.

Chapter 1

Drummond, J. C. and Wilbraham, A. (1939) *The Englishman's Food: A History of Five Centuries of English Diet*, Jonathan Cape, London.

WHO (2000) Global Water Supply and Sanitation Assessment: 2000 Report, World Health Organisation, Geneva; accessible via links to the WHO under Course Resources on the S320 website.

Chapter 2

Becker, J., Drucker, E., Enyong, P. and Marx, P. (2002) Availability of injectable antibiotics in a town market in Southwest Cameroon, *The Lancet Infectious Diseases*, **2**, pp. 325–6; accessible via http://infection.thelancet.com

CIDPC Canada (2002) Primary HIV anti-retroviral drug resistance in Canada (including summary of key studies in Western Europe and USA), *HIV/AIDS Epi Update*, April 2002; accessible at http://www.hc-sc.gc.ca/pphb-dgspsp/publicat/epiu-aepi/hiv-vih/drgres_e.html

Davies, E. (2000) Update on antiretroviral therapy, *Pharmaceutical Journal*, **264**, Issue 7079, pp. 96–7; accessible at http://www.pharmj.com/Editorial/20000115/education/antiretroviral.html

Goodyer, L. (2000) Travel Medicine: Malaria, *Pharmaceutical Journal*, **264**, Issue 7087, pp. 405–10; accessible at http://www.pharmj.com/Editorial/20000311/education/malaria.html

Jordan, R., Gold, L., Cummins, C. and Hyde, C. (2002) Systematic review and meta-analysis of evidence for increasing numbers of drugs in antiretroviral combination therapy, *British Medical Journal*, **324**, pp. 757–60; accessible via http://www.bmj.com

Kramer, A., Rudolph, P., Kamf, G. and Pittet, D. (2002) Limited efficacy of alcohol-based hand gels, *Lancet,* **359**, pp. 1489–90; accessible via http://www.thelancet.com (Open University Library e-Journal).

Levy, S. B. (2001) Antibacterial household products: cause for concern, *Emerging Infectious Diseases*, **7** (No.3 Supplement), pp. 512–5; accessible via http://infection.thelancet.com (Open University Library e-Journal).

Neill, F. (2002) The bacteria are going to win in the end, *The Times Magazine*, 11 May, pp. 26–30.

Radford, C. F., Minassian, D. C. and Dart, J. K. G. (2002) Acanthamoeba keratitis in England and Wales: incidence, outcome and risk factors, *British Journal of Opthalmology*, **86**, pp. 536–42.

Rosenthal, R. A., McAnally, C. L., McNamee, L.S. *et al.* (2000) Broad spectrum antimicrobial activity of a new multi-purpose disinfecting solution, *Contact Lens Association of Opthalmologists*, **26** (3), pp.120–6.

Singer, R. S., Finch, R., Wegener, H. C., Bywater, R., Walters, J. and Lipsitch, M. (2003) Antibiotic resistance – the interplay between antibiotic use in animals and human beings, *The Lancet Infectious Diseases*, **3**, pp. 47–51; accessible via http://infection.thelancet.com (Open University Library e-Journal).

Smith, C. R. (1947) Alcohol as a disinfectant against the tubercule bacillus, *Public Health Report,* **62**, pp.1285–95.

Price, D., Honeybourne, D., Little, P. *et al.* (2002) Community-aquired pneumonia mortality: a potential link to recent antibiotic prescribing trends in England and Wales (Abstract), *European Respiratory Journal*, **20**, (Suppl. 38), p. 397S.

Taylor, D. (2003) Fewer new drugs from the pharmaceutical industry (Editorial), *British Medical Journal*, **326**, pp. 408–9.

WHO UNICEF (2002) Oral rehydration salts (ORS): a new reduced osmolarity formulation, May 10, *Rehydration Project,* accessible at http://www.rehydrate.org/ors/who-unicef-statement.html

Yamey, G. and Torreele, E. (2002) The world's most neglected diseases (editorial), *British Medical Journal,* **325**, pp. 176–7; accessible via www.bmj.com

Chapter 3

Dellepiane, N., Griffiths, E. and Milstien, J. B. (2000) New challenges in assuring vaccine quality, *Bulletin of the World Health Organization*, **78** (2), pp. 155–62.

Lancet Infectious Diseases Newsdesk (2002) Drug companies asked to deliver on a low-cost menigitis vaccine, *The Lancet Infectious Diseases*, **2**, p. 650.

Taylor, L. H., Latham, S. M. and Woolhouse, M. E. J. (2001) Risk factors for human disease emergence, *Philosophical Transactions of the Royal Society of London* B, **356**, pp. 983–989.

WHO (2001) *Yellow Fever*, Fact Sheet 100 (last revised December 2001); accessible at http://www.who.int/inf-fs/en/fact100.html

Chapter 4

Armstrong Schellenberg, J. R. M., Abdulla, S., Nathan, R. *et al.* (2001) Effect of large-scale social marketing of insecticide-treated nets on child survival in rural Tanzania, *The Lancet*, **357**, pp. 1241–7.

Boot, M. T. and Cairncross, S. (eds) (1993) *Actions Speak: The study of hygiene behaviour in water and sanitation projects*, IRC International and Water Sanitation Centre and London School of Hygiene and Tropical Medicine, London.

Curtis, V. and Cairncross, S. (2003) Effect of washing hands with soap on diarrhoea risk in the community: a systematic review, *The Lancet Infectious Diseases*, **3**, pp. 275–81.

Curtis, C., Maxwell, C., Lemnge, M. *et al.* (2003) Scaling-up coverage with insecticide-treated nets against malaria in Africa: who should pay? *The Lancet Infectious Diseases*, **3**, pp. 304–7.

FSA (2002) *Catering Workers Hygiene Survey 2002*, Food Standards Agency, London; at http://www.foodstandards.gov.uk/hygcampaign/fhccateringsurvey

FSA (2003) *Consumer Attitudes Survey 2002*, Food Standards Agency, London; at http://www.foodstandards.gov.uk/hygcampaign/consumerresearch

Lengeler, C. (2001) Insecticide-treated bednets and curtains for preventing malaria (Cochrane Review), in *Cochrane Library*, **1**, Update Software, Oxford; accessible by following the links at http://www.cochraneconsumer.com/index.asp?SHOW=HotTopics

Mead, P. S., Slutsker, L., Dietz, V. *et al.* (1999) Food-related illness and death in the United States, *Emerging Infectious Diseases*, **5** (5), pp. 607–25.

Myer, L, Mathews, C. and Little, F. (2001) Condom gap in Africa is wider than study suggests (Letter), *British Medical Journal*, **323**, p. 937.

Palmer, S. R., Watkeys, J. E. M., Zamiri, I. *et al.* (1990) Outbreak of salmonella food poisoning amongst delegates at a medical conference, *Journal of the Royal College of Physicians of London*, **24** (1), pp. 26–9.

Shelton, J. D. and Johnston, B. (2001) Condom gap in Africa: evidence from donor agencies and key informants, *British Medical Journal*, **323**, p. 139.

UN (2000) *United Nations Millennium Declaration*, Resolution 55/2, adopted by the General Assembly of the United Nations, 18 September 2000, New York.

Victoria, C. G., Bryce, J., Fontaine, O. and Monasch, R. (2000) Reducing deaths from diarrhoea through oral rehydration therapy, *Bulletin of the World Health Organisation*, **78** (10), pp. 1246–55.

WHO (2000) *Overcoming Antimicrobial Resistance*, Infectious Disease Report 2000, World Health Organisation, Geneva; accessible at http://www.who.int/infectious-disease-report/2000/ (last accessed April 2003).

WHO/CDS/RBM (2000) *Country Updates: October 1998-June 2000,* Roll Back Malaria Campaign, World Health Organisation, Geneva; accessible at http://mosquito.who.int/cmc_upload/0/000/015/163/CountryUpdates.pdf (last accessed May 2003).

WHO (2002) *World Health Report 2002: Reducing Risks, Promoting Healthy Life,* World Health Organisation, Geneva.

Winslow, C. E. A. (1920) The untilled field of public health, *Modern Medicine,* **2**, p. 183.

World Bank (1993) *Investing in Health*, World Development Report 1993, Oxford University Press, Oxford.

Chapter 5

Braide, E. I., Ibanga, N., Johnson, M. *et al.*, (1994) Impact of JICA boreholes on the incidence of Guinea worm disease and school attendance in Enugu State, Calabar, Nigeria, *Nigeria Guinea Worm Eradication Programme.*

Cairncross, S., Braide, E. I. and Bugri, S. Z. (1996) Community participation in the eradication of guinea worm disease, *Acta Tropica*, **61**, pp. 121–36.

Cairncross, S., Muller, R. and Zagaria, N. (2002) Dracunculiasis (guinea worm disease) and the eradication initiative, *Clinical Microbiology Reviews,* **15**(2), pp. 223–46.

WHO (2002) Dracunculiasis eradication, *Weekly Epidemiological Record*, **77** (No.18), pp. 141–52 (accessible at http://www/who.int/wer).

WHO/CDS/CPE/CEE (2000) International Commission for the Certification of Dracunculiasis Eradication, Fourth Meeting: 15–17 February 2000, *Report and Recommendations*, World Health organisation, Geneva.

FURTHER SOURCES

Links to the online sources for all chapters may be accessed from the *Course Resources* section of the course website.

Chapter 2

Block, S. S. (ed.) (2001) *Disinfection, Sterilization and Preservation*, 5th edn., Lippincott, Williams and Wilkins, Philadelphia; particularly Chapter 12 on 'Alcohols' by Ali, Y., Dolan M. J., Fendler, E. J. and Larsen, E. L , and Chapter 13 on 'Surface-active Agents' by Merianos, J. J.

Denyer S. P. and Syewart, G. S. (1998) Mechanisms of action of disinfectants, *International Biodeterioration and. Biodegradation*, **41**, pp. 261–8.

Maillard J.-Y. J. (2002) Bacterial target sites for biocide action, *Applied Microbiology*, Symposium Supplement, **92**, pp. 6S–27S.

McDevitt, D., Payne, D. J., Holmes, D.J. and Rosenberg, M. J. (2002) Novel targets for the future development of antibacterial agents, *Applied Microbiology*, Symposium Supplement, **92**, pp. 28S–34S.

S320 *Reference* CD-ROM: S204 *Uniformity and Diversity*, Book 4, Macqueen, H. (ed.) (2001) *Microbes,* Chapter 7, The Open University, Milton Keynes.

ANSWERS TO QUESTIONS

QUESTION 1.1

The incidence (new cases) of TB fell steadily after about 1880 due to improvements in social and environmental conditions in the newly industrial towns and cities. Public health interventions to reduce overcrowding, increase living standards and improve food safety (particularly the bacterial contamination of milk), led to increased resistance to developing active TB, even though the majority of the population were infected with *M. tuberculosis.* From about 1900 to 1950, some reduction may have been achieved in the transmission of TB by people with active infection as a result of isolation in specialized TB hospitals and sanitaria. In the 1920s, the first vaccine (BCG) was developed and adopted for public use in France, though it took decades before it was adopted in some other countries (e.g. it was not used in the UK until 1954), and its effectiveness has remained variable. In the 1940s, transmission of TB was further reduced by the treatment of infectious patients with the first effective antibiotic, streptomycin. Currently, a range of different antibiotics are available and are prescribed in combinations to patients whose compliance with daily drug regimens may require careful monitoring in 'Directly Observed Treatment' programmes.

QUESTION 1.2

Several 'biological' constraints make cholera difficult to control. *Vibrio cholerae* occur naturally in aquatic environments such as estuaries and brackish water, where the local population may become infected as they bathe or fish, or use water for washing and cooking. Thus, there is an environmental reservoir that cannot be eradicated. Infected individuals who develop active disease shed huge numbers of cholera bacteria in the watery diarrhoea it classically induces, spreading the pathogens to close contacts and posing a high risk of contaminating drinking water and food. The vaccines developed to protect people against cholera either have limited effectiveness, or the protection is of short duration. Some antibiotics were originally quite effective against cholera, but the bacteria rapidly became resistant. The socio-economic constraints against effective control of cholera are evident in its global distribution; the areas where it remains endemic are among the poorest in the world, often without access to safe drinking water or adequate sanitation.

QUESTION 2.1

Alcohols, at effective concentrations, can kill bacteria quickly on contact (they are bactericidal) but do not kill bacterial spores. However, they prevent the development of any spores into active bacteria (they are sporistatic).

QUESTION 2.2

There is now a much greater awareness and understanding of potential long-term adverse effects of drugs on the recipient (e.g. carcinogenicity, mutagenicity, allergenicity, neurotoxicity), or in particular groups of patients (e.g. teratogenic effects on the foetus if drugs are taken during pregnancy; poor tolerance of the drug in people with concurrent health problems such as liver or kidney damage). Interactions with other drugs may also alter selective toxicity, since some chemical agents may act synergistically or antagonistically. In addition, Ehrlich was only concerned with drug toxicity in the patient, whereas modern drug safety testing is also concerned with reducing the damage to commensal organisms in the host and to other species in the wider environment.

QUESTION 2.3

Young children do not deactivate and eliminate chemical compounds as efficiently as older children and adults, so it persists in the body for longer. Thus, even after taking their smaller body size into account, a lower dose of the active ingredient is generally given, either because it is effective at that concentration and/or because higher doses might be toxic.

QUESTION 2.4

The most likely explanation is that the chemical is unable to penetrate the bacterial cell wall and interact with the enzyme. Alternatively, the chemical could have been inactivated in the body before it could reach its target. It may have been rapidly broken down by the host's own metabolic pathways for eliminating 'foreign' chemicals, or perhaps the conditions in the body (e.g. the pH) altered its conformation so it was no longer active. Or it could have been destroyed by the bacteria (e.g. some bacteria can inactivate beta-lactam antibiotics by secreting an enzyme that cleaves the beta-lactam ring).

QUESTION 2.5

Sulfonamide drugs are analogues of a naturally-occurring bacterial nutrient (*para*-aminobenzoic acid, or PABA), which bacteria require as the substrate for making folic acid. The drug competes with PABA for binding sites on an enzyme which catalyses the metabolism of PABA, in effect 'starving' the bacteria of folic acid. A member of the sulfonamide class, *para*-aminosalicylic acid (PAS), has some selectivity for mycobacteria, so it might have some prophylactic use in people who were known to have been exposed to someone with active (i.e. infectious) TB – although in practice, other more effective antitubercular drugs are likely to be used.

Nucleoside analogue reverse transcriptase inhibitors (NARTIs) compete with DNA nucleosides for binding sites on reverse transcriptase, the enzyme in retroviruses (such as HIV) that catalyses the transcription of the viral RNA genome into viral DNA. The transcription of the DNA chain is terminated at the point where the NNRTI molecule is incorporated instead of a DNA nucleoside. NARTIs have been used prophylactically to reduce the risk of HIV infection in people who have been accidentally exposed to the virus (e.g. health workers who suffer a 'needle-stick' injury) – although in recent years the non-nucleoside drugs (NNRTIs) have been shown to be more effective prophylactic agents.

QUESTION 2.6

Anopheles mosquitoes have been tackled directly with chemical insecticides, or indirectly by floating surfactants onto the surface of still water where they breed. The problems with these approaches are that insecticides and some surfactants are toxic or otherwise harmful to other species in the environment, the spraying regime has to be repeated routinely to replace the chemical agents as they are degraded, and the mosquito breeding sites may be inaccessible to chemical treatment. Insecticide treated bed-nets make a significant contribution to malaria prevention, and the use of insect-repellent creams or sprays on exposed skin is also recommended.

QUESTION 2.7

The first and most serious problem is that the drugs slow the progression to AIDS, but they do not eliminate HIV. Patients on HAART regimens often experience a range of unpleasant side effects, at least for a time. Drugs that were initially effective may become useless when the virus mutates and resistant strains quickly emerge. Consistent compliance with the multiple drug regimen is difficult because it involves several different medicines taken in a strict schedule in relation to meals. Poor compliance promotes the evolution of new drug-resistant strains. The drugs are very expensive, so they are beyond the reach of most HIV-infected people who are in the world's poorest countries. Patent protection lawsuits delayed access to cheaper generic drugs. Even if drugs are supplied at low cost to developing countries, the infrastructure is generally lacking to deliver them consistently and to ensure compliance with such a complex drug regimen, which must be taken life-long. Key opinion leaders have cast doubt on the need to supply HAART drugs to people with HIV and AIDS.

QUESTION 3.1

Both assertions are untrue. Active vaccines are mainly used prophylactically, i.e. to prevent the development of an infectious disease, but they can also be used therapeutically in people who have already been infected, in an attempt to boost the immune response and eliminate the infection, or at least slow the progression of the disease. Passive immunisation is also used in both ways: prophylactically in some infections (e.g. after exposure to a known source of rabies virus) to protect the person against developing the disease, and therapeutically after symptoms have developed in bacterial infections where the harmful agent is an exotoxin.

QUESTION 3.2

(a) Ramses V of Egypt, 1157 BC.

(b) Rhazes in *De Variolis et Morbillis Commentarius*, 910 AD.

(c) Hittite, Aztec, Inca, Roman, Athenian and many others.

(d) Lady Mary Whortley Montague in 1717 AD.

(e) Blindness

(f) Benjamin Jesty in 1774 AD.

(g) A chain of vaccinia infection was maintained in orphan children carried on the boats for this purpose. As each child developed vaccinia pustules, the infection was deliberately passed on to another child by arm-to-arm contact.

QUESTION 3.3

The current vaccine against smallpox is a live, attenuated strain of the cowpox virus (vaccinia), which induces cross-reacting immune responses against the variola virus, which causes smallpox and to which it is closely related. Very few vaccines are based on cross-reacting antigens. Research into new smallpox vaccines is very unlikely to use intact killed variola, because it would not meet safety critera. If even a few virions accidentally survive and cause smallpox infection in a vaccinee, they could 'escape' into the unvaccinated population to re-establish a lethal epidemic disease. If it proved possible to identify critical variola antigens that were also immunogenic, then safe subunit vaccines might be constructed that would induce a protective immune response. Alternatively, the genes encoding critical antigens could be cloned into harmless virus strains, which express them in the vaccine recipient. It might also be possible to construct a DNA vaccine to achieve the same outcome.

QUESTION 3.4

The combined DTP vaccine is more effective than when its components are used separately because both the diphtheria and tetanus toxoids act as adjuvants. They are added to some other vaccines (e.g. conjugate MenC) to enhance the immune response to vaccine antigens. The presence of certain bacterial proteins in a vaccine (among other effects) increases the expression of costimulatory molecules on antigen-presenting cells and this increases the activation of helper T cells, which stimulate other effector mechanisms.

QUESTION 3.5

The numerous genes encoding trypanosome antigens may recombine to produce new antigenic variants. So the immune response against these parasites is continually being overtaken. This raises the problem of which antigens to include in a vaccine, since potentially there are so many. Although sleeping sickness is a major cause of disease and disability in Africa, it does not occur in richer areas of the world, so there is less financial incentive to develop a vaccine that impoverished economies may be unable to afford. The incentive to develop a vaccine may also have been adversely affected by the recognition that vaccination can never eradicate the disease. There is a huge permanent reservoir of infection in cattle and other domestic and wild mammals, and the insect vector (tsetse flies) are endemic in a vast geographical area where control is extremely difficult.

QUESTION 3.6

Highly successful vaccines that have virtually eliminated an infection from a population for a prolonged period may have the effect of altering public perceptions about the importance of vaccine-associated risk compared to the perceived threat of the disease. When a disease has fallen to a very low level in a population, there is no longer any direct experience of its adverse consequences, which tend to be underestimated. Conversely, the importance attached to the risk from the vaccine (however low that may be) tends to increase among people who have to decide whether to accept it (particularly on behalf of their children), as the apparent threat from the disease declines.

QUESTION 4.1

Primary prevention strategies against malaria include chemoprophylaxis – taking drugs to protect against infection with malaria parasites before going into an endemic area, or at high-risk periods (e.g. during pregnancy); keeping skin covered, particularly from dusk to dawn; use of insect-repellent chemicals on exposed skin; routine use of bed-nets when sleeping; treating mosquito nets regularly with insecticide; spraying houses with insecticides against adult and larval mosquitoes; use of curtains across doors and windows; environmental engineering to prevent or destroy mosquito breeding sites; putting surfactant on the surface of pools used by mosquitoes for breeding; keeping water tanks covered. Secondary prevention includes providing education about the signs of malaria and the need to seek treatment as soon as possible; surveillance of individuals in communities in endemic regions (e.g. by blood testing) and administration of drugs to treat early cases of malaria. Tertiary prevention refers to treatment of the life-threatening complications of malaria (e.g. cerebral malaria), usually with intravenously administered drugs and fluids.

QUESTION 4.2

TB sanitaria reflect the traditional emphasis on tackling an infectious disease by isolating cases, providing hospital-based care focused on individuals, employing the health sector as the sole provider of services, and leaving decision-making powers entirely in the hands of health professionals. The DOTs programme comes much closer to the ideals of the 'new public health' because, even though its prime purpose is to ensure compliance with the drug regimen, it supports individuals within their communities and involves many agencies (including volunteers) in the delivery of the programme, which is (ideally) negotiated to ensure community-wide participation. However, it does not tackle the socio-economic conditions that increase the spread of TB, it is not involved in the development of disease-prevention strategies, nor does it contribute to the promotion of 'positive health' for all.

QUESTION 4.3

One factor may simply have been the difficulty in changing the ritual of washing clothes in the canal at the traditional places, but more pragmatic reasons are also suggested by this scenario. Washing clothes in the village generates a substantial volume of waste water, which – if poured onto the ground day after day – may create muddy pools where mosquitos can breed, or even create habitats for the snails that act as the intermediate hosts for schistosoma. Waste water on the ground could obstruct routes through the village and gradually erode the mud bricks and undermine the houses. Tipping it into the latrines will make them fill up faster and shorten the time to when a new latrine pit has to be dug.

QUESTION 4.4

Table 4.1 shows that Uganda had the lowest expectation of healthy life for babies born in 2000, compared to the other countries shown; its spending on health was only slightly higher than that of Tanzania in most years and the amount per capita did not change between 1995 and 2000. Figure 4.6 reveals that, in the 1990s, Uganda achieved an increase of approximately 45 percentage points (from 5% to 50%) in the proportion of children with diarrhoea who received oral rehydration therapy – the largest increase of any country in this sample. The implication of these observations is that although the poor economic circumstances of Uganda in this period has limited its spending on the health of its population, nevertheless some progress has been made in increasing the uptake of a low-cost, technologically simple intervention (ORS), which can be expected to have saved children's lives. Community health workers are the most likely agents to be involved in promoting the uptake of ORS by the parents of young children in Uganda.

QUESTION 5.1

Even in endemic countries, dracunculiasis does not occur in urban areas where piped water is supplied, and it is rare in rural communities where the principal sources of drinking water are fast-running streams or deep wells, because the intermediate host (cyclops) cannot survive in these environments. It inhabits still, shallow water, such as natural pools and step-wells, where people are most likely to stand as they draw water, or seek relief from the burning pain of a guinea worm as it emerges.

QUESTION 5.2

The association of areas of endemicity with still, shallow water sources can be broken by drilling boreholes and installing pumps to access deep water, but they are costly to construct and maintain and geological problems may be insuperable. Cheaper wells can be constructed in some areas that enable water to be drawn out without people entering the water, but they do not overcome the problem of workers needing to drink from natural pools out in the fields. Transmission of guinea worm larvae can be interrupted by filtering drinking water through a cloth (or a mesh-ended straw) to remove infected cyclops, but villagers may not appreciate the necessity to do this 'now' to prevent a disease that emerges almost a year later, and supplies of mesh filters may be inadequate.

ACKNOWLEDGEMENTS

Grateful acknowledgment is made to the following sources for permission to reproduce material in this book:

Figures

Figure 1.2: WHO/TDR/Crump; *Figure 2.1*: Royal Pharmaceutical Society of Great Britain; *Figure 2.2*: Rosenthal, R. A. *et al.*(2000) 'Broad spectrum antimicrobial activity of a new multi-purpose disinfecting solution', CLAO (Contact Lens Association of Ophthalmologists, Inc), Journal, Vol. 26, No 3, CLAO; *Figure 2.8*: Roitt, I. *et al*. (1996) 'Secondary Immunodeficiencies', *Immunology*, 4th edn, Elsevier Science; *Figure 2.9*: Mark Boulton/ICCE; *Figure 2.10*: WHO/TDR/Andy Crump; *Figure 3.1*: Edward Jenner Museum; *Figure 3.2*: Private Collection/ Bridgeman; *Figure 3.3*: Roitt, I. *et al*. (1998) 'Effect of vaccination on the incidence of viral disease', *Immunology*, 5th edn, Elsevier Science Limited.; *Figure 3.4*: Science Photo Library; *Figure 3.5* Bio-Rad Laboratories; *Figure 3.9*: Reprinted from Armstrong, D., and Cohen, J. (1999) *Infectious Diseases*, Elsevier Science Limited; *Figure 3.11*: WHO/TDR/M. D. Gupte; *Figure 4.1*: H. Schwarzbach/UNEP/ Still Pictures; *Figurse 4.2, 4.4 and 4.7*: WHO/TDR/Martel; *Figure 4.3*: WHO/TDR/ Crump; *Figure 4.5*: Courtesy of Ken Hudson; *Figure 4.8*: WHO/HPR/TDR/Crump; *Figure 4.10*: Mike Levers/Open University; *Figure 5.1*: Courtesy of Dr A. Tayeh; *Figure 5.2, 5.4, 5.7, 5.9 and 5.10*: Courtesy of Ralph Muller; *Figure 5.5*: Cairncross, S. *et al*. 'Dracunculiasis (Guinea Worm Disease) and the eradication initiative', *Clinical Microbiology Reviews*, April 2002, American Society for Microbiology; *Figure 5.8*: Braide, E. I. *et al.*(1994) Impact of JICA boreholes on the incidence of Guinea worm disease and school attendance in Enugu State, Calbar, Nigeria: Nigeria Guinea Worm Eradication Programme.

Tables

Table 2.1: Reprinted with permission from Elsevier Science (*The Lancet*, 2002, **359**, p. 1490).

Every effort has been made to contact copyright holders. If any have been inadvertently overlooked, the publishers will be pleased to make the necessary arrangements at the first opportunity.

INDEX

Note: Entries in **bold** are key terms. Page numbers referring to information that is given only in a figure or caption are printed in *italics*.